Meet Minitab 15

for Windows®

January 2007

ISBN 978-0925636-51-5

Printed in the USA

© 2006 by Minitab Inc. All rights reserved.

Revised Printing, May 2007

Table of Contents

1 Getting Started 1-1
    Objectives 1-1
    Overview 1-1
    Typographical Conventions in this Book 1-2
    The Story 1-3
    Starting Minitab 1-3
    Opening a Worksheet 1-4
    What Next 1-6

2 Graphing Data 2-1
    Objectives 2-1
    Overview 2-1
    Exploring the Data 2-2
    Examining Relationships Between Two Variables 2-8
    Using Graph Layout and Printing 2-11
    Saving Projects 2-13
    What Next 2-14

3 Analyzing Data 3-1
    Objectives 3-1
    Overview 3-1
    Displaying Descriptive Statistics 3-2
    Performing an ANOVA 3-4
    Using Minitab's Project Manager 3-10
    What Next 3-12

4 Assessing Quality 4-1
    Objectives 4-1
    Overview 4-1
    Evaluating Process Stability 4-2
    Evaluating Process Capability 4-8
    What Next 4-10

5 **Designing an Experiment** 5-1

    Objectives. 5-1

    Overview 5-1

    Creating an Experimental Design 5-2

    Viewing the Design. 5-5

    Entering Data 5-5

    Analyzing the Design 5-6

    Drawing Conclusions 5-9

    What Next 5-11

6 **Using Session Commands** 6-1

    Objectives. 6-1

    Overview 6-1

    Enabling and Typing Commands 6-2

    Rerunning a Series of Commands 6-5

    Repeating Analyses with Execs 6-6

    What Next 6-8

7 **Generating a Report** 7-1

    Objectives. 7-1

    Overview 7-1

    Using the ReportPad 7-2

    Saving a Report. 7-6

    Copying a Report to a Word Processor 7-6

    Using Embedded Graph Editing Tools. 7-7

    What Next 7-9

8 **Preparing a Worksheet** 8-1

    Objectives. 8-1

    Overview 8-1

    Getting Data from Different Sources 8-2

    Preparing the Worksheet for Analysis. 8-5

    What Next 8-11

9 Customizing Minitab 9-1

Objectives 9-1

Overview 9-1

Setting Options 9-2

Creating a Custom Toolbar 9-3

Assigning Shortcut Keys 9-5

Restoring Minitab's Default Settings 9-6

What Next 9-7

10 Getting Help 10-1

Objectives 10-1

Overview 10-1

Getting Answers and Information 10-2

Minitab Help Overview 10-4

Help 10-6

StatGuide 10-8

Session Command Help 10-10

What Next 10-11

11 Reference 11-1

Objectives 11-1

Overview 11-1

The Minitab Environment 11-2

Minitab Data 11-5

Quick Reference 11-6

Index I-1

Documentation
Additional Minitab Products
How to Order Additional Products

1

Getting Started

Objectives

In this chapter, you:

- Learn how to use *Meet Minitab*, page 1-1
- Start Minitab, page 1-3
- Open and examine a worksheet, page 1-4

Overview

Meet Minitab introduces you to the most commonly used features in Minitab. Throughout the book, you use functions, create graphs, and generate statistics. The contents of *Meet Minitab* relate to the actions you need to perform in your own Minitab sessions. You use a sampling of Minitab's features to see the range of features and statistics that Minitab provides.

Most statistical analyses require a series of steps, often directed by background knowledge or by the subject area you are investigating. Chapters 2 through 5 illustrate the analysis steps in a typical Minitab session:

- Exploring data with graphs
- Conducting statistical analyses and procedures
- Assessing quality
- Designing an experiment

Chapters 6 through 9 provide information on:

- Using shortcuts to automate future analyses
- Generating a report
- Preparing worksheets
- Customizing Minitab to fit your needs

Chapter 10, *Getting Help*, includes information on getting answers and using Minitab Help features. Chapter 11, *Reference*, provides an overview of the Minitab environment, a discussion about the types and forms of data that Minitab uses, and quick-reference tables of actions and statistics available in Minitab.

You can work through *Meet Minitab* in two ways:

- From beginning to end, following the story of a fictional online bookstore through a common workflow

- By selecting a specific chapter to familiarize yourself with a particular area of Minitab

Meet Minitab introduces dialog boxes and windows when you need them to perform a step in the analysis. As you work, look for these icons for additional information:

         Provides notes and tips

         Suggests related topics in Minitab Help and StatGuide

Typographical Conventions in this Book

Enter	Denotes a key, such as the **Enter** key.
Alt + D	Denotes holding down the first key and pressing the second key. For example, while holding down the Alt key, press the D key.
File ➤ Exit	Denotes a menu command, in this case choose **Exit** from the **File** menu. Here is another example: **Stat ➤ Tables ➤ Tally Individual Variables** means open the **Stat** menu, then open the **Tables** submenu, and finally choose **Tally Individual Variables**.
Click **OK**.	Bold text clarifies dialog box items and buttons and Minitab commands.
Enter *Pulse1*.	Italic text specifies text you need to enter.

The Story

An online book retail company has three regional shipping centers that distribute orders to consumers. Each shipping center uses a different computer system to enter and process order information. To integrate all orders and use the most efficient method company wide, the company wants to use the same computer system at all three shipping centers.

Throughout this book, you analyze data from the shipping centers as you learn to use Minitab. You create graphs and conduct statistical analyses to determine which computer system is the most efficient and results in the shortest delivery time.

After you identify the most efficient computer system, you focus on the data from this center. First, you create control charts to see whether the center's shipping process is in control. Then, you conduct a capability analysis to see whether the process is operating within specification limits. Finally, you conduct a designed experiment to further improve the shipping center's processes.

Additionally, you learn about session commands, generating a report, preparing a worksheet, and customizing Minitab.

Starting Minitab

Before you begin your analysis, start Minitab and examine the layout of the windows.

Start Minitab

1 From the Windows Taskbar, choose **Start ➤ Programs ➤ Minitab Solutions ➤ Minitab 15 Statistical Software English**.

Minitab opens with two main windows visible:

- The Session window displays the results of your analysis in text format. Also, in this window, you can enter commands instead of using Minitab's menus.

- The Data window contains an open worksheet, which is similar in appearance to a spreadsheet. You can open multiple worksheets—each in a different Data window.

Session window

Data window:
- Columns
- Rows
- Cells

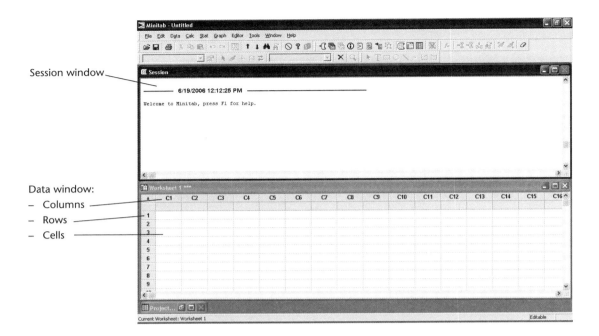

 For more information on the Minitab environment, see *The Minitab Environment* on page 11-2.

Opening a Worksheet

You can open a new, empty worksheet at any time. You can also open one or more files that contain data. When you open a file, you copy the contents of the file into the current Minitab project. Any changes you make to the worksheet while in the project will not affect the original file.

The data for the three shipping centers are stored in the worksheet SHIPPINGDATA.MTW.

 In some cases, you will need to prepare your worksheet before you begin an analysis. For information on setting up a worksheet, see Chapter 8, *Preparing a Worksheet*.

Open a worksheet

1 Choose **File ➤ Open Worksheet**.

2 Click **Look in Minitab Sample Data folder**, near the bottom of the dialog box.

3 In the Sample Data folder, double-click Meet Minitab.

You can change the default folder for opening and saving Minitab files by choosing **Tools ➤ Options ➤ General**.

4 Choose SHIPPINGDATA.MTW, then click **Open**. If you get a

message box, check **Do not display this message again**, then click **OK**. To restore this message for every time you open a worksheet, return to Minitab's default settings. See *Restoring Minitab's Default Settings* on page 9-6.

Examine worksheet

The data are arranged in columns, which are also called *variables*. The column number and name are at the top of each column. Each row in the worksheet represents a case, which is information on a single book order.

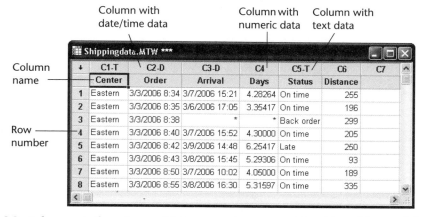

Minitab accepts three types of data: numeric, text, and date/time. This worksheet contains each type.

The data include:

- Shipping center name

- Order date

- Delivery date

- Number of delivery days

- Delivery status ("On time" indicates that the book shipment was received on time; "Back order" indicates that the book is not currently in stock; "Late" indicates that the book shipment was received six or more days after ordered)

- Distance from shipping center to delivery location

 For more information about data types, see *Minitab Data* on page 11-5.

What Next

Now that you have a worksheet open, you are ready to start using Minitab. In the next chapter, you use graphs to check the data for normality and examine the relationships between variables.

2
Graphing Data

Objectives

In this chapter, you:

- Create and interpret an individual value plot, page 2-2
- Create a histogram with groups, page 2-4
- Edit a histogram, page 2-5
- Arrange multiple histograms on the same page, page 2-6
- Access Help, page 2-8
- Create and interpret scatterplots, page 2-9
- Edit a scatterplot, page 2-10
- Arrange multiple graphs on the same page, page 2-12
- Print graphs, page 2-13
- Save a project, page 2-13

Overview

Before conducting a statistical analysis, you can use graphs to explore data and assess relationships among the variables. Also, graphs are useful to summarize findings and to ease interpretation of statistical results.

You can access Minitab's graphs from the Graph and Stat menus. Built-in graphs, which help you to interpret results and assess the validity of statistical assumptions, are also available with many statistical commands.

Graph features in Minitab include:

- A pictorial gallery from which to choose a graph type
- Flexibility in customizing graphs, from subsetting of data to specifying titles and footnotes

■ Ability to change most graph elements, such as fonts, symbols, lines, placement of tick marks, and data display, after the graph is created

■ Ability to automatically update graphs

This chapter explores the shipping center data you opened in the previous chapter, using graphs to compare means, explore variability, check normality, and examine the relationship between variables.

For more information on Minitab graphs:

■ Go to *Graphs* in the Minitab Help index and then double-click the *overview* entry for details on Minitab graphs. To access the Help index, choose **Help ➤ Help**, then click the **Index** tab.

■ Choose **Help ➤ Tutorials ➤ Session One: Graphing Data** for a step-by-step tutorial on using Minitab graphs and editing tools.

Exploring the Data

Before conducting a statistical analysis, you should first create graphs that display important characteristics of the data.

For the shipping center data, you want to know the mean delivery time for each shipping center and how variable the data are within each shipping center. You also want to determine if the shipping center data follow a normal distribution so you that you can use standard statistical methods for testing the equality of means.

Create an individual value plot

You suspect that delivery time is different for the three shipping centers. Create an individual value plot to compare the shipping center data.

1 If not continuing from the previous chapter, choose **File ➤ Open Worksheet**. If continuing from the previous chapter, go to step 4.

2 Click **Look in Minitab Sample Data folder**, near the bottom of the dialog box.

3 In the Sample Data folder, double-click Meet Minitab, then choose SHIPPINGDATA.MTW. Click **Open**.

4 Choose **Graph ➤ Individual Value Plot**.

For most graphs, Minitab displays a pictorial gallery. Your gallery choice determines the available graph creation options.

5 Under **One Y**, choose **With Groups**, then click **OK**.

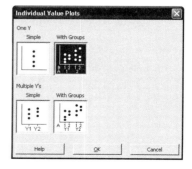

6 In **Graph variables**, enter *Days*.

7 In **Categorical variables for grouping (1-4, outermost first)**, enter *Center*.

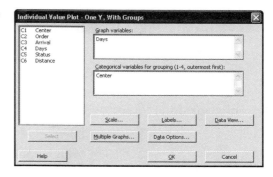

To create a graph, you only need to complete the main dialog box. However, you can click any button to open dialog boxes to customize your graph.

The list box on the left shows the variables from the worksheet that are available for the analysis. The boxes on the right display the variables that you select for the analysis.

8 Click **Data View**. Check **Mean connect line**.

9 Click **OK** in each dialog box.

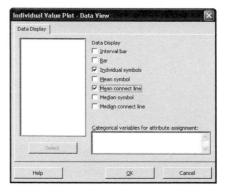

To select variables in most Minitab dialog boxes, you can: double-click the variables in the variables list box; highlight the variables in the list box, then choose **Select**; or type the variables' names or column numbers.

Graph window output

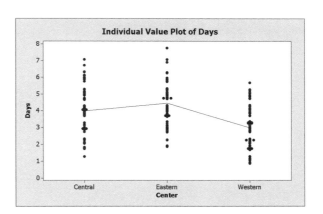

Interpret results

The individual value plots show that each center has a different mean delivery time. The Western center has a lower shipping time than the Central and Eastern centers. The variation within each shipping center seems about the same.

Create a grouped histogram

Another way to compare the three shipping centers is to create a grouped histogram, which displays the histograms for each center on the same graph. The grouped histogram will show how much the data from each shipping center overlap.

1 Choose **Graph ➤ Histogram**.

2 Choose **With Fit And Groups**, then click **OK**.

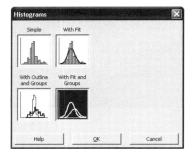

3 In **Graph variables**, enter *Days*.

4 In **Categorical variables for grouping (0-3)**, enter *Center*.

5 Click **OK**.

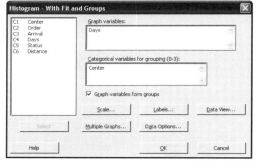

Graph window output

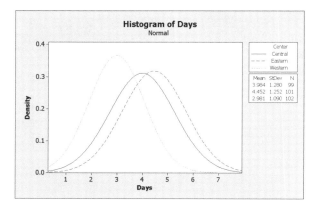

Interpret results

As you saw in the individual value plot, the means for each center are different. The mean delivery times are:

Central — 3.984 days

Eastern — 4.452 days

Western — 2.981 days

The grouped histogram shows that the Central and Eastern centers are similar in mean delivery time and spread of delivery time. In contrast, the Western center mean delivery time is shorter and less spread out. Chapter 3, *Analyzing Data*, shows how to detect stastistically significant differences among means using analysis of variance.

 If your data change, Minitab can automatically update graphs. For more information, go to *Updating graphs* in the Minitab Help index.

Edit histogram

Editing graphs in Minitab is easy. You can edit virtually any graph element. For the histogram you just created, you want to:

■ Make the header text in the legend (the table with the center information) bold

■ Modify the title

Change the legend table header font

1 Double-click the legend.

2 Click the **Header Font** tab.

3 Under **Style**, check **Bold**.

4 Click **OK**.

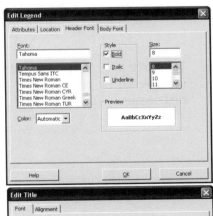

Change the title

1 Double-click the title (*Histogram of Days*).

2 In **Text**, type *Histogram of Delivery Time*.

3 Click **OK**.

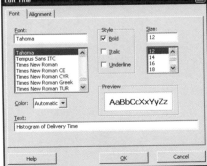

Graph window output

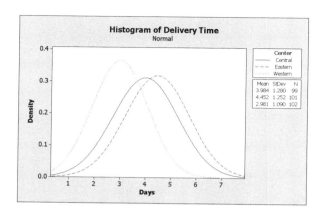

Interpret results

The histogram now features a bold font for the legend heading and a more descriptive title.

In addition to editing individual graphs, you can change the default settings for future graphs.

■ To affect general graph settings, such as font attributes, graph size, and line types, choose **Tools ➤ Options ➤ Graphics**.

■ To affect graph-specific settings, such as the scale type on histograms or the method for calculating the plotted points on probability plots, choose **Tools ➤ Options ➤ Individual Graphs**.

The next time you open an affected dialog box, your preferences are reflected.

Create a paneled histogram

To determine if the shipping center data follow a normal distribution, create a paneled histogram of the time lapse between order and delivery date.

1 Choose **Graph ➤ Histogram**.

2 Choose **With Fit**, then click **OK**.

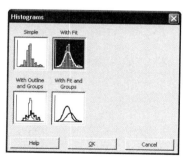

3 In **Graph variables**, enter *Days*.

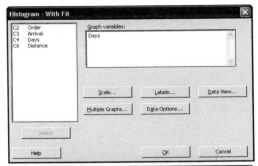

4 Click **Multiple Graphs**, then click the **By Variables** tab.

5 In **By variables with groups in separate panels**, enter *Center*.

6 Click **OK** in each dialog box.

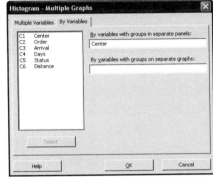

Graph window output

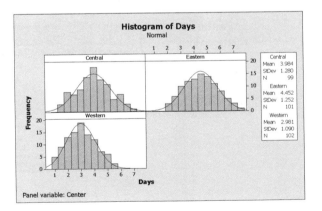

Interpret results

The delivery times for each center are approximately normally distributed as shown by the distribution curves exhibiting the same pattern.

 If you have fewer than 50 observations, you may want to use a normal probability plot (**Graph ➤ Probability Plot**) to assess normality.

Examining Relationships Between Two Variables

Graphs can help identify whether associations are present among variables and the strength of any associations. Knowing the relationship among variables can help to guide further analyses and determine which variables are important to analyze.

Because each shipping center serves a small regional delivery area, you suspect that distance to delivery site does not greatly affect delivery time. To verify this suspicion and eliminate distance as a potentially important factor, examine the relationship between delivery time and delivery distance.

Access Help   To find out which graph shows the relationship between two variables, use Minitab Help.

1 Choose **Help ➤ Help**.

2 Click the **Index** tab.

3 In **Type in the keyword to find**, type *Graphs* and then double-click the *Overview* entry to access the Help topic.

4 In the Help topic, under the heading **Types of graphs**, click **Examine relationships between pairs of variables**.

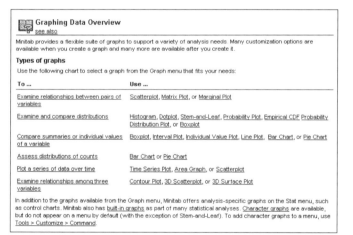

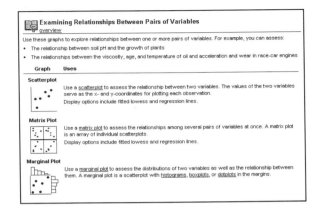

This Help topic suggests that a scatterplot is the best choice to see the relationship between delivery time and delivery distance.

 For help on any Minitab dialog box, click **Help** in the lower left corner of the dialog box or press ⌐F1⌐. For more information on Minitab Help, see Chapter 10, *Getting Help*.

Create a scatterplot

1 Choose **Graph ➤ Scatterplot**.

2 Choose **With Regression**, then click **OK**.

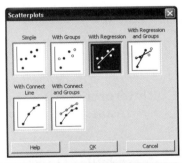

3 Under **Y variables**, enter *Days*. Under **X variables**, enter *Distance*.

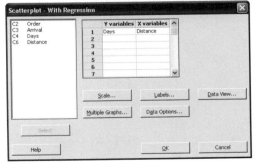

4 Click **Multiple Graphs**, then click the **By Variables** tab.

5 In **By variables with groups in separate panels**, enter *Center*.

6 Click **OK** in each dialog box.

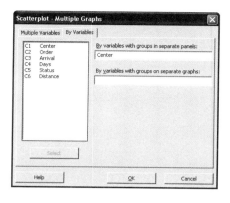

Graph window output

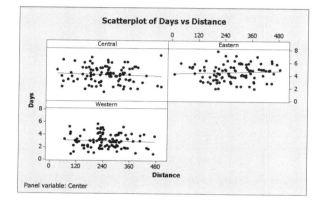

Interpret results

The points on the scatterplot exhibit no apparent pattern at any of the three centers. The regression line for each center is relatively flat, suggesting that the proximity of a delivery location to a shipping center does not affect the delivery time.

Edit scatterplot

To help your colleagues quickly interpret the scatterplot, you want to add a footnote to the plot.

1 Click the scatterplot to make it active.

2 Choose **Editor ➤ Add ➤ Footnote**.

3 In **Footnote**, type *Relationship between delivery time and distance from shipping center.*

4 Click **OK**.

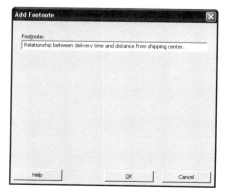

Graph window output

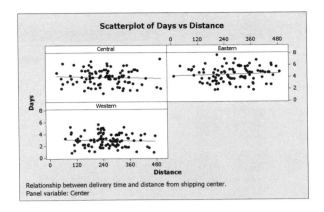

Interpret results

The scatterplot now features a footnote that provides a brief interpretation of the results.

Using Graph Layout and Printing

Use Minitab's graph layout tool to place multiple graphs on the same page. You can add annotations to the layout and edit the individual graphs within the layout.

To show your supervisor the preliminary results of the graphical analysis of the shipping data, display all four graphs on one page.

 When you issue a Minitab command that you previously used in the same session, Minitab remembers the dialog box settings. To set a dialog box back to its defaults, press F3 .

Create graph layout

1 With the scatterplot active, choose **Editor ➤ Layout Tool**. The active graph, the scatterplot, is already included in the layout.

A list of all open graphs

Buttons used to move graphs to and from the layout

The next graph to be moved to the layout

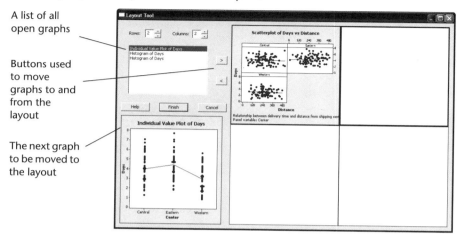

2 Click the scatterplot and drag it to the bottom right corner of the layout.

3 Click [>] to place the individual value plot in the upper-left corner of the layout.

4 Click [>] to place the grouped histogram in the upper-right corner.

5 Click [>] to place the paneled histogram in the lower-left corner.

6 Click **Finish**.

Graph window output

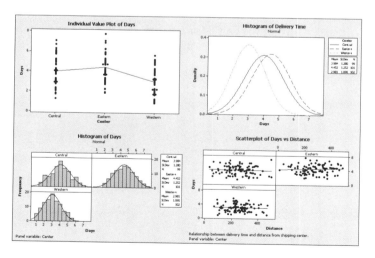

  If the worksheet data change after you create a layout, Minitab does not automatically update the graphs in the layout. You must re-create the layout with the updated individual graphs.

Annotate the layout

You want to add a descriptive title to the layout.

1 Choose **Editor ➤ Add ➤ Title**.

2 In **Title**, type *Graphical Analysis of Shipping Center Data*. Click **OK**.

Graph window output

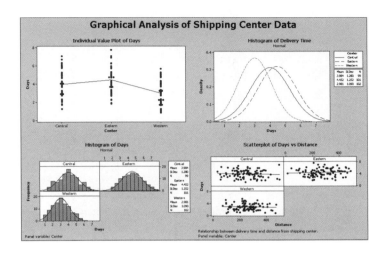

Print graph layout

You can print an individual graph or a layout just as you would any other Minitab window.

1 Click the Graph window to make it active, then choose **File ➤ Print Graph**.

2 Click **OK**.

Saving Projects

Minitab data are saved in worksheets. You can also save Minitab projects which can contain multiple worksheets. A Minitab project contains all your work, including the data, Session window output, graphs, history of your session, ReportPad contents, and dialog box settings. When you open a project, you can resume working where you left off.

It is a good practice to save your work to a location outside the Program Files folder. While working through this book, files are saved to a Meet Minitab folder in the My Documents folder. You can save files to a location of your choice (outside the Program Files folder).

Save a Minitab project

Save all of your work in a Minitab project.

1 Choose **File ➤ Save Project As**.

2 Navigate to the folder in which you want to save your files.

3 In **File name**, type *MY_GRAPHS.MPJ*. Minitab automatically adds the extension .MPJ to the file name when you save the project.

4 Click **Save**.

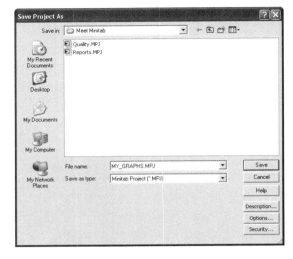

 If you close a project before saving it, Minitab prompts you to save the project.

What Next

The graphical output indicates that the three shipping centers have different delivery times for book orders. In the next chapter, you display descriptive statistics and perform an analysis of variance (ANOVA) to test whether the differences among the shipping centers are statistically significant.

3

Analyzing Data

Objectives

In this chapter, you:

- Display and interpret descriptive statistics, page 3-2
- Perform and interpret a one-way ANOVA, page 3-4
- Display and interpret built-in graphs, page 3-4
- Access the StatGuide, page 3-8
- Use the Project Manager, page 3-10

Overview

The field of statistics provides principles and methodologies for collecting, summarizing, analyzing, and interpreting data, and for drawing conclusions from analysis results. Statistics can be used to describe data and to make inferences, both of which can guide decisions and improve processes and products.

Minitab provides:

- Many statistical methods organized by category, such as regression, ANOVA, quality tools, and time series
- Built-in graphs to help you understand the data and validate results
- The ability to display and store statistics and diagnostic measures

This chapter introduces Minitab's statistical commands, built-in graphs, StatGuide, and Project Manager. You want to assess the number of late and back orders, and test whether the difference in delivery time among the three shipping centers is statistically significant.

For more information on Minitab's statistical features, go to *Stat menu* in the Minitab Help index.

Displaying Descriptive Statistics

Descriptive statistics summarize and describe the prominent features of data.

Use Display Descriptive Statistics to find out how many book orders were delivered on time, how many were late, and the number that were initially back ordered for each shipping center.

Display descriptive statistics

1 If continuing from the previous chapter, choose **File ➤ New**, then choose **Minitab Project**. Click **OK**. Otherwise, just start Minitab.

2 Choose **File ➤ Open Worksheet**.

3 Click **Look in Minitab Sample Data folder**, near the bottom of the dialog box.

4 In the Sample Data folder, double-click Meet Minitab, then choose SHIPPINGDATA.MTW. Click **Open**. This worksheet is the same one you used in Chapter 2, *Graphing Data*.

5 Choose **Stat ➤ Basic Statistics ➤ Display Descriptive Statistics**.

6 In **Variables**, enter *Days*.

7 In **By variables (optional)**, enter *Center Status*.

For most Minitab commands, you only need to complete the main dialog box to execute the command. But, you can often use subdialog boxes to modify the analysis or display additional output, like graphs.

8 Click **Statistics**.

9 Uncheck **First quartile**, **Median**, **Third quartile**, **N nonmissing**, and **N missing**.

10 Check **N total**.

11 Click **OK** in each dialog box.

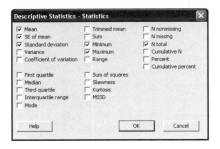

 Changes made in the Statistics subdialog box affect the current session only. To change the default settings for future sessions, use **Tools ➤ Options ➤ Individual Commands ➤ Display Descriptive Statistics**. When you open the Statistics subdialog box again, it reflects your preferences.

Session window output

Descriptive Statistics: Days

Results for Center = Central

Variable	Status	Total Count	Mean	SE Mean	StDev	Minimum	Maximum
Days	Back order	6	*	*	*	*	*
	Late	6	6.431	0.157	0.385	6.078	7.070
	On time	93	3.826	0.119	1.149	1.267	5.983

Results for Center = Eastern

Variable	Status	Total Count	Mean	SE Mean	StDev	Minimum	Maximum
Days	Back order	8	*	*	*	*	*
	Late	9	6.678	0.180	0.541	6.254	7.748
	On time	92	4.234	0.112	1.077	1.860	5.953

Results for Center = Western

Variable	Status	Total Count	Mean	SE Mean	StDev	Minimum	Maximum
Days	Back order	3	*	*	*	*	*
	On time	102	2.981	0.108	1.090	0.871	5.681

The Session window displays text output, which you can edit, add to the ReportPad, and print. The ReportPad is discussed in Chapter 7, *Generating a Report*.

Interpret results

The Session window presents each center's results separately. Within each center, you can find the number of back, late, and on-time orders in the Total Count column.

- The Eastern shipping center has the most back orders (8) and late orders (9).

- The Central shipping center has the next greatest number of back orders (6) and late orders (6).

- The Western shipping center has the smallest number of back orders (3) and no late orders.

You can also review the Session window output for the mean, standard error of the mean, standard deviation, minimum, and maximum of order status for each center. These statistics are not given for back orders because no delivery information exists for these orders.

Performing an ANOVA

One of the most commonly used methods in statistical decisions is hypothesis testing. Minitab offers many hypothesis testing options, including t-tests and analysis of variance. Generally, a hypothesis test assumes an initial claim to be true, then tests this claim using sample data.

Hypothesis tests include two hypotheses: the null hypothesis (denoted by H_0) and the alternative hypothesis (denoted by H_1). The null hypothesis is the initial claim and is often specified using previous research or common knowledge. The alternative hypothesis is what you may believe to be true.

Based on the graphical analysis you performed in the previous chapter and the descriptive analysis above, you suspect that the difference in the average number of delivery days (response) across shipping centers (factor) is statistically significant. To verify this, perform a one-way ANOVA, which tests the equality of two or more means categorized by a single factor. Also, conduct a Tukey's multiple comparison test to see which shipping center means are different.

Perform an ANOVA

1 Choose **Stat ➤ ANOVA ➤ One-Way**.

2 In **Response**, enter *Days*. In **Factor**, enter *Center*.

   In many dialog boxes for statistical commands, you can choose frequently used or required options. Use the subdialog box buttons to choose other options.

3 Click **Comparisons**.

4 Check **Tukey's, family error rate**, then click **OK**.

5 Click **Graphs**.

For many statistical commands, Minitab includes built-in graphs that help you interpret the results and assess the validity of statistical assumptions.

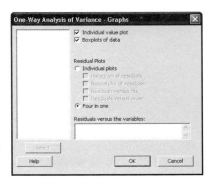

6 Check **Individual value plot** and **Boxplots of data**.

7 Under **Residual Plots**, choose **Four in one**.

8 Click **OK** in each dialog box.

Session window output

One-way ANOVA: Days versus Center

```
Source   DF      SS     MS      F      P
Center    2  114.63  57.32  39.19  0.000
Error   299  437.28   1.46
Total   301  551.92

S = 1.209   R-Sq = 20.77%   R-Sq(adj) = 20.24%
```

```
                               Individual 95% CIs For Mean Based on
                               Pooled StDev
Level     N   Mean  StDev   -----+---------+---------+---------+----
Central  99  3.984  1.280                        (----*---)
Eastern 101  4.452  1.252                            (----*----)
Western 102  2.981  1.090   (----*---)
                            -----+---------+---------+---------+----
                             3.00      3.50      4.00      4.50

Pooled StDev = 1.209
```

```
Tukey 95% Simultaneous Confidence Intervals
All Pairwise Comparisons among Levels of Center

Individual confidence level = 98.01%


Center = Central subtracted from:

Center   Lower   Center   Upper  ---------+---------+---------+---------+
Eastern  0.068   0.468    0.868                       (---*---)
Western -1.402  -1.003   -0.603    (---*---)
                                 ---------+---------+---------+---------+
                                     -1.0       0.0       1.0       2.0
```

```
Center = Eastern subtracted from:

Center    Lower   Center  Upper   ---------+---------+---------+---------+
Western  -1.868  -1.471  -1.073   (---*---)
                                  ---------+---------+---------+---------+
                                        -1.0      0.0       1.0       2.0
```

Interpret results

The decision-making process for a hypothesis test can be based on the probability value (p-value) for the given test.

- If the p-value is less than or equal to a predetermined level of significance (α-level), then you reject the null hypothesis and claim support for the alternative hypothesis.

- If the p-value is greater than the α-level, you fail to reject the null hypothesis and cannot claim support for the alternative hypothesis.

In the ANOVA table, the p-value (0.000) provides sufficient evidence that the average delivery time is different for at least one of the shipping centers from the others when α is 0.05. In the individual 95% confidence intervals table, notice that none of the intervals overlap, which supports the theory that the means are statistically different. However, you need to interpret the multiple comparison results to see where the differences exist among the shipping center averages.

Tukey's test provides two sets of multiple comparison intervals:

- Central shipping center mean subtracted from Eastern and Western shipping center means

- Eastern shipping center mean subtracted from Western center mean

The first interval in the first set of the Tukey output is 0.068 to 0.868. That is, the mean delivery time of the Eastern center minus that of the Central center is somewhere between 0.068 and 0.868 days. Because the interval does not include zero, the difference in delivery time between the two centers is statistically significant. The Eastern center's deliveries take longer than the Central center's deliveries. You similarly interpret the other Tukey test results. The means for all shipping centers differ significantly because all of the confidence intervals exclude zero. Therefore, all the shipping centers have significantly different average delivery times. The Western shipping center has the fastest mean delivery time (2.981 days).

Graph window output

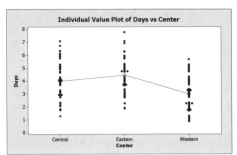

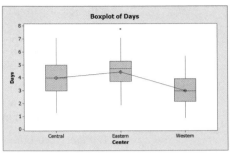

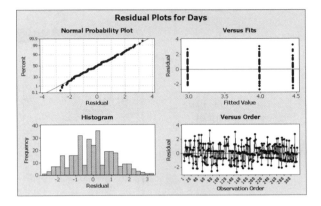

Interpret results

The individual value plots and boxplots indicate that the delivery time varies by shipping center, which is consistent with the graphs from the previous chapter. The boxplot for the Eastern shipping center indicates the presence of one outlier (indicated by ∗), which is an order with an unusually long delivery time.

Use residual plots, available with many statistical commands, to check statistical assumptions:

- Normal probability plot—to detect nonnormality. An approximately straight line indicates that the residuals are normally distributed.

- Histogram of the residuals—to detect multiple peaks, outliers, and nonnormality. The histogram should be approximately symmetric and bell-shaped.

- Residuals versus the fitted values—to detect nonconstant variance, missing higher-order terms, and outliers. The residuals should be scattered randomly around zero.

- Residuals versus order—to detect time-dependence of residuals. The residuals should exhibit no clear pattern.

For the shipping data, the four-in-one residual plots indicate no violations of statistical assumptions. The one-way ANOVA model fits the data reasonably well.

 In Minitab, you can display each of the residual plots on a separate page. You can also create a plot of the residuals versus the variables.

Access StatGuide

You want more information on how to interpret a one-way ANOVA, particularly Tukey's multiple comparison test. Minitab StatGuide provides detailed information about the Session and Graph window output for most statistical commands.

1 Place your cursor anywhere in the one-way ANOVA Session window output.

2 Click 🖼 on the Standard toolbar.

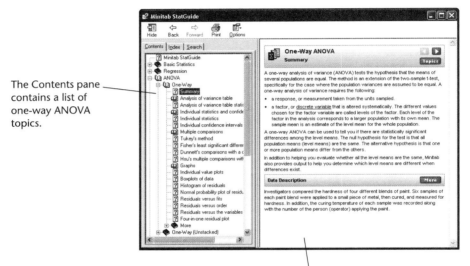

The Contents pane contains a list of one-way ANOVA topics.

The main StatGuide pane contains a one-way ANOVA summary.

3 You want to learn more about Tukey's multiple comparison method. In the Contents pane, click **Tukey's method**.

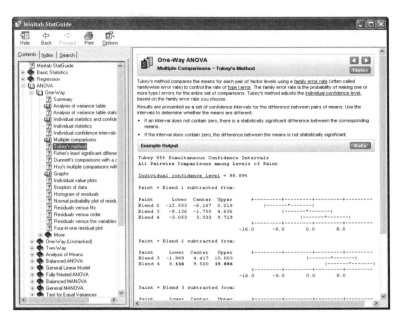

The StatGuide displays

  – information about Tukey's method

  – Tukey's method example

  – guidance for interpreting the example output when you scroll down

4 If you like, use ◀ ▶ to browse through the one-way ANOVA topics.

5 In the StatGuide window, click ✕ to close it.

 For more information about using the StatGuide, see *StatGuide* on page 10-8.

Save project   Save all your work in a Minitab project.

1 Choose **File ➤ Save Project As**.

2 Navigate to the folder in which you want to save your files.

3 In **File name**, type *MY_STATS.MPJ*.

4 Click **Save**.

Using Minitab's Project Manager

Now you have a Minitab project that contains a worksheet, several graphs, and Session window output from your analyses. The Project Manager helps you navigate, view, and manipulate parts of your Minitab project.

Use the Project Manager to view the statistical analyses you just conducted.

Open Project Manager

1   To access the Project Manager, click 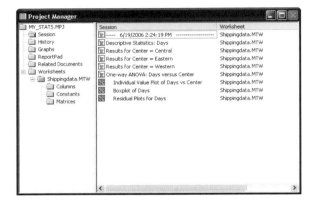 on the Project Manager toolbar or press Ctrl + I .

You can easily view the Session window output and graphs by choosing from the list in the right pane. You can also use the icons on the Project Manager toolbar to access different output.

For more information, see *Project Manager* on page 11-3.

View Session window output

You want to review the one-way ANOVA output. To become familiar with the Project Manager toolbar, use the Show Session Folder icon ⊞ on the toolbar, which opens the Session window.

1   Click ⊞ on the Project Manager toolbar.

2   Double-click **One-way ANOVA: Days versus Center** in the left pane.

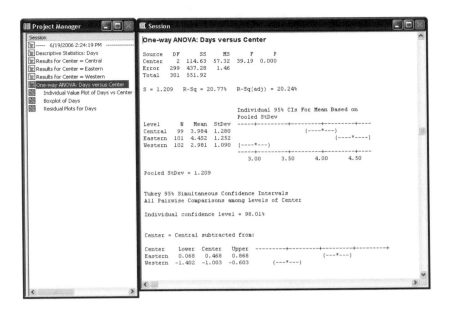

The Project Manager displays the one-way ANOVA Session window output in the right pane.

View graphs
You also want to view the boxplot again. Use the Show Graphs icon 🖼 on the toolbar.

1 Click 🖼 on the Project Manager toolbar.

2 In the left pane, double-click **Boxplot of Days by Center** in the left pane.

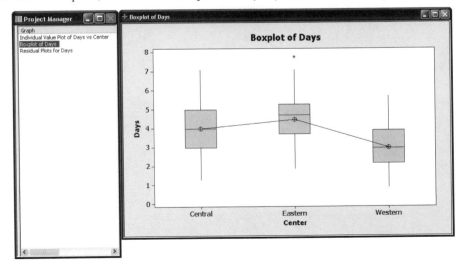

The Project Manager displays the boxplot in the Graph window in the right pane.

What Next

The descriptive statistics and ANOVA results indicate that the Western center has the fewest late and back orders and the shortest delivery time. In the next chapter, you create a control chart and conduct a capability analysis to investigate whether the Western shipping center's process is stable over time and is capable of operating within specifications.

4

Assessing Quality

Objectives

In this chapter, you:

- Set options for control charts, page 4-2
- Create and interpret control charts, page 4-3
- Update a control chart, page 4-5
- View subgroup information, page 4-7
- Add a reference line to a control chart, page 4-7
- Conduct and interpret a capability analysis, page 4-9

Overview

Quality is the degree to which products or services meet the needs of customers. Common objectives for quality professionals include reducing defect rates, manufacturing products within specifications, and standardizing delivery time.

Minitab offers a wide array of methods to help you evaluate quality in an objective, quantitative way: control charts, quality planning tools, and measurement systems analysis (gage studies), process capability, and reliability/survival analysis. This chapter discusses control charts and process capability.

Features of Minitab control charts include:

- The ability to choose how to estimate parameters and control limits, as well as display tests for special causes and historical stages.
- Customizable attributes, such as adding a reference line, changing the scale, and modifying titles. As with other Minitab graphs, you can customize control charts when and after you create them.

Features of process capability commands include:

■ The ability to analyze many data distribution types, such as normal, exponential, Weibull, gamma, Poisson, and binomial.

■ An array of charts that can be used to verify that the process is in control and that the data follow the chosen distribution.

The graphical and statistical analyses conducted in the previous chapter show that the Western shipping center has the fastest delivery time. In this chapter, you determine whether the center's process is stable (in control) and capable of operating within specifications.

Evaluating Process Stability

Use control charts to track process stability over time and to detect the presence of special causes, which are unusual occurrences that are not a normal part of the process.

Minitab plots a process statistic—such as a subgroup mean, individual observation, weighted statistic, or number of defects—versus a sample number or time. Minitab draws the:

■ Center line at the average of the statistic

■ Upper control limit (UCL) at 3 standard deviations above the center line

■ Lower control limit (LCL) at 3 standard deviations below the center line

For all control charts, you can modify Minitab's default chart specifications. For example, you can define the estimation method for the process standard deviation, specify the tests for special causes, and display process stages by defining historical stages.

 For additional information on Minitab's control charts, go to *Control Charts* in the Minitab Help index.

Set options for control charts

Before you create a control chart for the book shipping data, you want to specify options different from Minitab's defaults for testing the randomness of the data for all control charts.

The Automotive Industry Action Group (AIAG) suggests using the following guidelines to test for special causes:

■ Test 1: 1 point > 3 standard deviations from center line

■ Test 2: 9 points in a row on the same side of center line

■ Test 3: 6 points in a row, all increasing or all decreasing

Also, in accordance with AIAG guidelines, for all future control charts, you want to use a value of 7 for tests 2 and 3. You can easily do this by setting options for your control charts analysis. When you set options, affected dialog boxes automatically reflect your preferences.

1   Choose **Tools ➤ Options ➤ Control Charts and Quality Tools ➤ Tests**.

2   Check the first three tests.

3   Under **K** for the second test, change the value to 7.

4   Under **K** for the third test, change the value to 7.

5   Click **OK**.

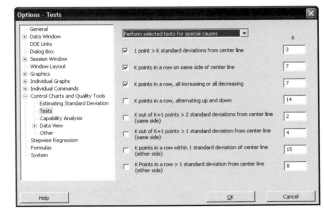

 If you set options, you can restore Minitab's default settings at any time. For more information, see *Restoring Minitab's Default Settings* on page 9-6.

Create X̄ and S chart

Now you are ready to create a control chart to see whether the delivery process is stable over time. You randomly select 10 samples for 20 days to examine changes in the mean and variability of delivery time. Create an X̄ and S chart with which you can monitor the process mean and variability simultaneously. Use X̄ and S charts when you have subgroups of size 9 or more.

1   If continuing from the previous chapter, choose **File ➤ New**, then choose **Minitab Project**. Click **OK**. Otherwise, just start Minitab.

2   Choose **File ➤ Open Project**.

3   Navigate to C:\Program Files\Minitab 15\English\Sample Data\Meet Minitab. (Adjust this if you chose to install Minitab to a location other than the default.)

4   Choose QUALITY.MPJ. Click **Open**.

5   Choose **Stat ➤ Control Charts ➤ Variables Charts for Subgroups ➤ Xbar-S**.

To create a control chart, you only need to complete the main dialog box. However, you can click any button to select options for customizing your chart.

6 Choose **All observations for a chart are in one column**, then enter *Days*.

7 In **Subgroup sizes**, enter *Date*.

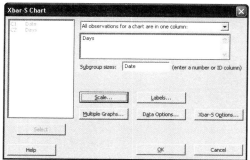

8 Click **Xbar-S Options**, then click the **Tests** tab. Notice this dialog box reflects the tests and test values you specified earlier. (See *Set options for control charts* on page 4-2.)

You can click any tab to open dialog boxes to customize your control chart. Available tabs depend on whatever is appropriate for the chart type. Parameters, Estimate, Display, and Storage are available for all control charts. Stages, Tests, S Limits, and Box-Cox are available for most charts. Other options are available for specific charts.

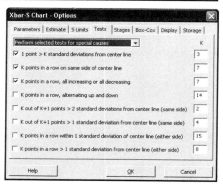

9 Click **OK** in each dialog box.

Graph window output

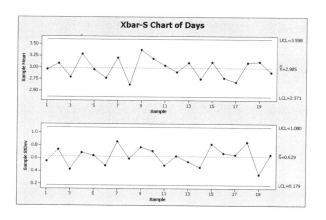

Interpret
$\overline{X}$ and S chart

The data points for the Western shipping center fall within the bounds of the control limits, and do not display any nonrandom patterns. Therefore, the process mean and process standard deviation appear to be in control (stable). The mean ($\overline{\overline{X}}$), is 2.985, and the average standard deviation ($\overline{S}$) is 0.629.

Update
control chart

Graph updating allows you to update a graph when the data change without re-creating the graph. Graph updating is available for all graphs in the Graph menu (except Stem-and-Leaf) and all control charts.

After creating the $\overline{X}$ and S chart, the Western shipping center manager gives you more data collected on 3/23/2006. Add the data to the worksheet and update the control chart.

Add the data to the worksheet

You need to add both date/time data to C1 and numeric data to C2.

1 Click the Data window to make it active.

2 Place your cursor in any cell in C1, then press End to go to the bottom of the worksheet.

3 To add the date 3/23/2006 to rows 201–210:

- First, type 3/23/2006 in row 201 in C1.

- Then, select the cell containing 3/23/2006, place the cursor over the Autofill handle in the lower-right corner of the highlighted cell. When the mouse is over the handle, a cross symbol (+) appears. Press Ctrl and drag the cursor to row 210 to fill the cells with the repeated date value. When you hold Ctrl down, a superscript cross appears above the Autofill cross symbol (++), indicating that repeated, rather than sequential, values will be added to the cells.

↓	C1-D	C2	C3
	Date	Days	
195	3/22/2006	2.50	
196	3/22/2006	2.85	
197	3/22/2006	2.69	
198	3/22/2006	1.83	
199	3/22/2006	3.59	
200	3/22/2006	2.82	
201	3/23/2006		
202			
203			
204			

Quality.MTW ***

4 Add the following data to C2, starting in row 201:

3.60 2.40 2.80 3.21 2.40 2.75 2.79 3.40 2.58 2.50

If the data entry arrow is facing downward, pressing (Enter) moves the cursor to the next cell down.

Data entry arrow ——

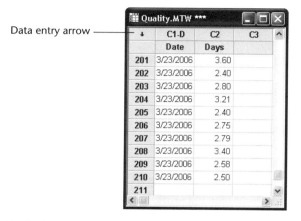

5 Verify that you entered the data correctly.

Update the control chart

1 Right-click the $\overline{X}$ and S chart and choose **Update Graph Now**.

*Graph
window
output*

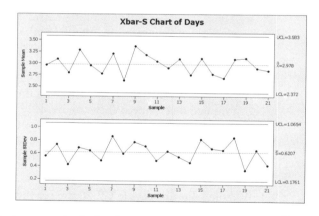

The $\overline{X}$ and S chart now includes the new subgroup. The mean ($\overline{\overline{X}}$ = 2.978) and standard deviation ($\overline{S}$ = 0.6207) have changed slightly, but the process still appears to be in control.

To update all graphs and control charts automatically:
1 Choose **Tools ➤ Options ➤ Graphics ➤ Other Graphics Options**.
2 Check **On creation, set graph to update automatically when data change**.

View subgroup information

As with any Minitab graph, when you move your mouse over the points in a control chart, you see various information about the data.

You want to find out the mean of sample 9, the subgroup with the largest mean.

1   Move your mouse over the data point for sample 9.

Graph window output

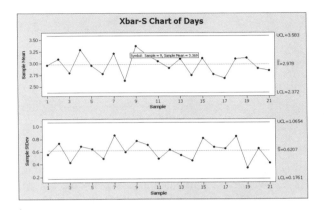

Interpret results

The data tip shows that sample 9 has a mean delivery time of 3.369 days.

Add reference line

A goal for the online bookstore is for all customers to receive their orders in 3.33 days (80 hours) on average, so you want to compare the average delivery time for the Western shipping center to this target. You can show the target level on the $\bar{X}$ chart by adding a reference line.

1   Right-click the $\bar{X}$ chart (the top chart), and choose **Add ➤ Reference Lines**.

2   In **Show reference lines at Y values**, type 3.33.

3   Click **OK**.

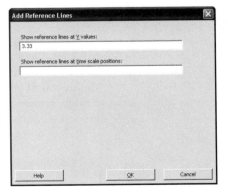

Graph window output

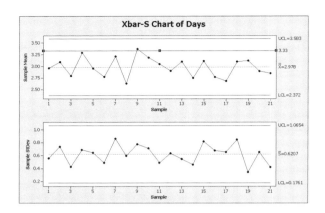

Interpret results

The center line ($\overline{\overline{X}}$) is well below the reference line, indicating that, on average, the Western shipping center delivers books faster than the target of 3.33 days. Only subgroup 9 has a delivery time that falls above the reference line (> 3.33).

Evaluating Process Capability

After you determine that a process is in statistical control, you want to know whether the process is capable—does it meet specifications and produce "good" parts or results? You determine capability by comparing the spread of the process variation to the width of the specification limits. If the process is not in control before you assess its capability, you may get incorrect estimates of process capability.

In Minitab, you can assess process capability graphically by drawing capability histograms and capability plots. These graphs help you assess the distribution of the data and verify that the process is in control. Capability indices, or statistics, are a simple way of assessing process capability. Because process information is reduced to a single number, you can use capability statistics to compare the capability of one process to another. Minitab offers capability analysis for many distribution types, including normal, exponential, Weibull, gamma, Poisson, and binomial.

 For more information on process capability, go to *Process Capability* in the Minitab Help index.

Conduct capability analysis

Now that you know the delivery process is in control, conduct a capability analysis to determine whether the book delivery process is within specification limits and results in acceptable delivery times. The target value of the delivery process is 3.33 days. The upper specification limit (USL) is 6 (an order that is received after 6 days is considered late); no lower specification limit (LSL) is identified. The distribution is approximately normal, so you can use a normal capability analysis.

1 Choose **Stat ➤ Quality Tools ➤ Capability Analysis ➤ Normal**.

2 Under **Data are arranged as**, choose **Single column**. Enter *Days*.

3 In **Subgroup size**, enter *Date*.

4 In **Upper spec**, type 6.

5 Click **Options**. In **Target (adds Cpm to table)**, type 3.33.

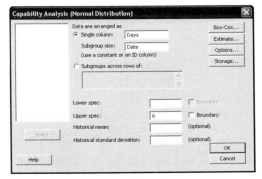

As with other Minitab commands, you can modify a capability analysis either by specifying information in the main dialog box or by clicking one of the subdialog box buttons.

6 Click **OK** in each dialog box.

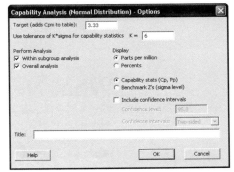

Graph window output

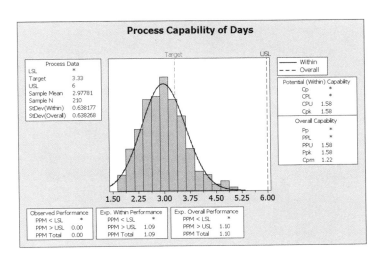

Process Capability of Days

Interpret results

All the potential and overall capability statistics are larger than 1.33 (a generally accepted minimum value), indicating the Western shipping center's process is capable and, therefore, delivers orders in an acceptable amount of time.

The Cpm value (the ratio of the specification spread, USL – LSL, to the square root of the mean squared deviation from the target value) is 1.22, which indicates that the process does not meet the target value. The $\overline{X}$ chart with the reference line shows that the process average fell below the target value, indicating favorable results. You conclude that customers, on average, are getting their orders sooner than the goal of 3.33 days.

 For more information on how to interpret capability analyses, go to the capability analysis topics in the StatGuide.

Save project

Save all of your work in a Minitab project.

1 Choose **File ➤ Save Project As**.

2 Navigate to the folder in which you want to save your files.

3 In **File name**, type *MY_QUALITY.MPJ*.

4 Click **Save**.

What Next

The quality analysis indicates that the Western shipping center's process is in control and is capable of meeting specification limits. In the next chapter, you design an experiment and analyze the results to investigate ways to further improve the order and delivery process at the Western shipping center.

5

Designing an Experiment

Objectives

In this chapter, you:

- Become familiar with designed experiments in Minitab, page 5-1
- Create a factorial design, page 5-2
- View a design and enter data in the worksheet, page 5-5
- Analyze a design and interpret results, page 5-6
- Create and interpret main effects and interaction plots, page 5-9

Overview

Design of experiments (DOE) capabilities provide a method for simultaneously investigating the effects of multiple variables on an output variable (response). These experiments consist of a series of runs, or tests, in which purposeful changes are made to input variables or factors, and data are collected at each run. Quality professionals use DOE to identify the process conditions and product components that influence quality and then determine the input variable (factor) settings that maximize results.

Minitab offers four types of designed experiments: factorial, response surface, mixture, and Taguchi (robust). The steps you follow in Minitab to create, analyze, and graph an experimental design are similar for all design types. After you conduct the experiment and enter the results, Minitab provides several analytical and graphing tools to help you understand the results. While this chapter demonstrates the typical steps for creating and analyzing a factorial design, you can apply these steps to any design you create in Minitab.

Features of Minitab DOE commands include:

- Catalogs of experimental designs from which you can choose, to make creating a design easier

- Automatic creation and storage of your design once you have specified its properties

- Ability to display and store diagnostic statistics, to help you interpret the results

- Graphs that assist you in interpreting and presenting the results

In this chapter, you want to further improve the amount of time it takes to get orders to customers from the Western shipping center. After evaluating many potentially important factors, you decide to investigate two factors that may decrease the time to prepare an order for shipment: the order processing system and packing procedure.

The Western center is experimenting with a new order processing system and you want to determine if it will speed up order preparation. The center also has two different packing procedures and you want to investigate which one is more efficient. You decide to conduct a factorial experiment to find out which combination of factors results in the shortest time to prepare an order for shipment. The results of this experiment will help you make decisions about the order processing system and packing procedures used in the shipping center.

 For more information on the types of designs that Minitab offers, go to *DOE* in the Minitab Help index.

Creating an Experimental Design

Before you can enter or analyze measurement data in Minitab, you must first create an experimental design and store it in the worksheet. Depending on the requirements of your experiment, you can choose from a variety of designs. Minitab helps you select a design by providing a list of all the available designs. Once you have chosen the design and its features, Minitab automatically creates the design and stores it in the worksheet for you.

Select design   You want to create a factorial design to examine the relationship between two factors, order processing system and packing procedure, and the time it takes to prepare an order for shipping.

1 If continuing from the previous chapter, choose **File ➤ New**, then choose **Minitab Project**. Click **OK**. Otherwise, just start Minitab.

2 Choose **Stat ➤ DOE ➤ Factorial ➤ Create Factorial Design**.

When you create a design in Minitab, initially only two buttons are enabled, **Display Available Designs** and **Designs**. The other buttons are enabled after you complete the **Designs** subdialog box.

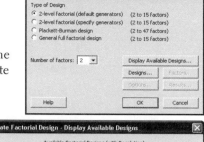

3 Click **Display Available Designs**.

For most design types, Minitab displays all the possible designs and number of required runs in the **Display Available Designs** dialog box.

4 Click **OK** to return to the main dialog box.

5 Under **Type of Design**, choose **2-level factorial (default generators)**.

6 In **Number of factors**, choose 2.

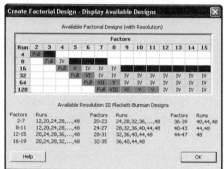

7 Click **Designs**.

The box at the top shows all available designs for the design type and the number of factors you chose. In this example, because you are conducting a factorial design with two factors, you have only one option: a full factorial design with four runs. A two-level design with two factors has 2^2 (or four) possible factor combinations.

8 In **Number of replicates for corner points**, choose 3.

9 Click **OK** to return to the main dialog box. Notice that Minitab enables the remaining buttons.

Name factors and set factor levels

Minitab enters the names and levels you enter for each factor into the worksheet and uses the names as the labels for the factors on the analysis output and graphs. If you do not enter factor levels, Minitab sets the low level at −1 and the high level at 1.

1 Click **Factors**.

2 Click the first row of the **Name** column to
   change the name of the first factor. Then, use
   the arrow keys to navigate within the table,
   moving across rows or down columns. In the
   row for:

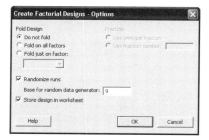

- **Factor A**, type *OrderSystem* in **Name**, *New*
  in **Low**, and *Current* in **High**. Under **Type**, choose **Text**.

- **Factor B**, type *Pack* in **Name**, *A* in **Low**, and *B* in **High**. Under **Type**, choose
  Text.

3 Click **OK** to return to the main dialog box.

**Randomize
and store
design**

By default, Minitab randomizes the run order of all design types, except Taguchi
designs. Randomization helps to ensure that the model meets certain statistical
assumptions and can also help reduce the effects of factors not included in the study.

Setting the base for the random data generator ensures you obtain the same run
order every time you create the design. While you usually would not do this in
practice, setting the base gives the same run order that is used in this example.

1 Click **Options**.

2 In **Base for random data generator**, type 9.

3 Make sure **Store design in worksheet** is
   checked. Click **OK** in each dialog box.

Viewing the Design

Every time you create a design, Minitab stores design information and factors in worksheet columns. Open the Data window to see the structure of a typical design. You can also open the worksheet DOE.MTW in the Meet Minitab data folder, which includes the design and the response data.

View design

1 Choose **Window ➤ Worksheet 1.**

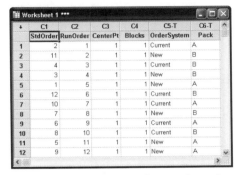

The RunOrder column (C2), which is randomly determined, indicates the order in which you should collect data. If you do not randomize a design, the StdOrder and RunOrder columns are the same.

In this example, because you did not add center points or block the design, Minitab sets all the values in C3 and C4 to 1. The factors are stored in columns C5 and C6, labeled OrderSystem and Pack. Because you entered the factor levels in the **Factors** subdialog box, you see the actual levels in the worksheet.

You can use **Stat ➤ DOE ➤ Display Design** to switch back and forth between a random and standard order display, and between a coded and uncoded display in the worksheet.

To change the factor settings or names, use **Stat ➤ DOE ➤ Modify Design**. If you only need to change the factor names, you can type them directly in the Data window.

Entering Data

After you conduct the experiment and collect the data, you can enter the data into the worksheet. The characteristic you measure is called a response.

In this example, you measure the number of hours needed to prepare an order for shipment. You obtained the following data from the experiment:

14.72 9.62 13.81 7.97 12.52 13.78 14.64 9.41 13.89 13.89 12.57 14.06

Enter data into worksheet

1 In the Data window, click the column name cell of C7 and type *Hours*.

2 Type the observed hours listed above into the Hours column of the Data window.

You can enter data in any columns except in those containing design information. You can also enter multiple responses for an experiment, one per column.

  Print a data collection form by choosing **File ➤ Print Worksheet** and making sure **Print Grid Lines** is checked. Use this form to record measurements while you conduct the experiment.

Analyzing the Design

Now that you have created a design and collected the response data, you can fit a model to the data and generate graphs to evaluate the effects. Use the results from the fitted model and graphs to see which factors are important for reducing the number of hours needed to prepare an order for shipment.

Fit a model

Because you have created and stored a factorial design, Minitab enables the **DOE ➤ Factorial** menu commands **Analyze Factorial Design** and **Factorial Plots**. At this point, you can fit a model or generate plots, depending on the design. In this example, you fit the model first.

1 Choose **Stat ➤ DOE ➤ Factorial ➤ Analyze Factorial Design**.

2 In **Responses**, enter *Hours*.

You must enter a response column before you can open the subdialog boxes.

3   Click **Terms**. Check to make sure that A:
    OrderSystem, B: *Pack* and *AB* are in the **Selected
    Terms** box.

    When analyzing a design, always use the **Terms**
    subdialog box to select the terms to include in the
    model. You can add or remove factors and
    interactions by using the arrow buttons. Use the
    check boxes to include blocks and center points in
    the model.

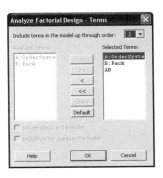

4   Click **OK**.

5   Click **Graphs**.

6   Under **Effects Plots**, check **Normal** and
    Pareto.

    Effects plots are only available in
    factorial designs. Residual plots, helpful
    in checking model assumptions, can be
    displayed for all design types.

7   Click **OK** in each dialog box.

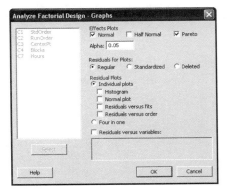

Identify important effects

You can use both the Session window output and the two effects plots to determine
which effects are important to your process. First, look at the Session window output.

Session window output

Factorial Fit: Hours versus OrderSystem, Pack

```
Estimated Effects and Coefficients for Hours (coded units)

Term                Effect    Coef   SE Coef       T      P
Constant                    12.573    0.1929   65.20  0.000
OrderSystem          3.097    1.548    0.1929    8.03  0.000
Pack                -2.320   -1.160    0.1929   -6.01  0.000
OrderSystem*Pack     1.730    0.865    0.1929    4.49  0.002


S = 0.668069     PRESS = 8.0337
R-Sq = 93.79%    R-Sq(pred) = 86.02%   R-Sq(adj) = 91.46%
```

```
Analysis of Variance for Hours (coded units)

Source                DF    Seq SS    Adj SS    Adj MS      F      P
Main Effects           2   44.9152   44.9152   22.4576  50.32  0.000
2-Way Interactions     1    8.9787    8.9787    8.9787  20.12  0.002
Residual Error         8    3.5705    3.5705    0.4463
  Pure Error           8    3.5705    3.5705    0.4463
Total                 11   57.4645


Estimated Coefficients for Hours using data in uncoded units

Term                      Coef
Constant               12.5733
OrderSystem             1.54833
Pack                   -1.16000
OrderSystem*Pack        0.865000


Alias Structure
I
OrderSystem
Pack
OrderSystem*Pack
```

You fit the full model, which includes the two main effects and the two-way interaction. Use the p-values (P) in the Estimated Effects and Coefficients table to determine which effects are significant. Using α = 0.05, the main effects for order processing system (OrderSystem) and packing procedure (Pack) and the OrderSystem∗Pack interaction are statistically significant; that is, their p-values are less than 0.05.

Interpret effects plots

Next, evaluate the normal probability plot and the Pareto chart of the standardized effects to see which effects influence the response, Hours.

1 To make the normal probability plot the active window, choose **Window ➤ Effects Plot for Hours**.

Significant terms are identified by a square symbol. OrderSystem (A), Pack (B), and OrderSystem∗Pack (A∗B) are significant (α = 0.05).

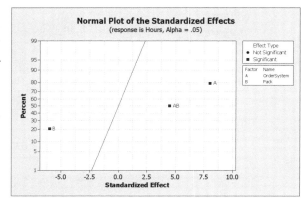

2 To make the Pareto chart the active window, choose **Window ➤ Effects Pareto for Hours**.

Minitab displays the absolute value of the effects on the Pareto chart. Any effects that extend beyond the reference line are significant at the default level of 0.05.

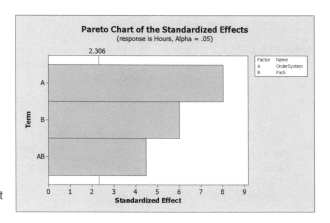

OrderSystem (A), Pack (B) and OrderSystem∗Pack (A∗B) are all significant ($\alpha = 0.05$).

Drawing Conclusions

Display factorial plots

Minitab provides design-specific graphs you can use to interpret your results.

In this example, you generate two factorial plots that enable you to visualize the effects—a main effects plot and an interaction plot.

1　Choose **Stat ➤ DOE ➤ Factorial ➤ Factorial Plots**.

2　Check **Main Effects Plot**, then click **Setup**.

3　In **Responses,** enter *Hours*.

4　Select the terms you want to plot:

- Click A:*OrderSystem* under **Available**. Then click ▹ to move A:*OrderSystem* factor to **Selected**.

- Repeat these actions to move B:*Pack* to **Selected**. Click **OK**.

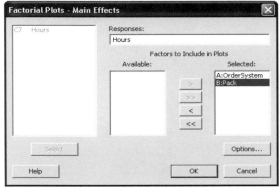

5　Check **Interaction Plot**, then click **Setup**.

6　Repeat steps 3 and 4.

7 Click **OK** in each dialog box.

Evaluate plots   Examine the plot that shows the effect of using the new versus current order processing system, or using packing procedure A versus B. These one-factor effects are called main effects.

1 Choose **Window ➤ Main Effects Plot for Hours** to make the main effects plot active.

This point shows the mean of all runs using the current order processing system.

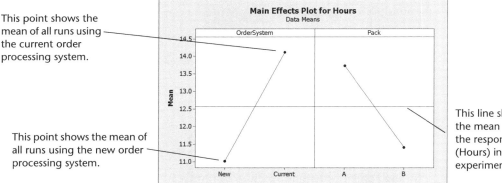

This point shows the mean of all runs using the new order processing system.

This line shows the mean of all the response (Hours) in the experiment.

The order processing system and packing procedure have a similar effect on order preparation time. That is, the line connecting the mean responses for the new and current order processing system has a slope similar to slope of the line connecting the mean response for packing procedure A and packing procedure B. The plot also indicates that orders using:

- The new order processing system took less time than orders that used the current order processing system.

- Packing procedures B took less time than orders that used packing procedure A

If there were no significant interactions between the factors, a main effects plot would adequately describe where you can get the biggest payoff for changes to your process. Because the interaction in this example is significant, you should next examine the interaction plot. A significant interaction between two factors can affect the interpretation of the main effects.

2 Choose **Window ➤ Interaction Plot for Hours** to make the interaction plot active.

The vertical scale (y-axis) is in units of the response (Hours).

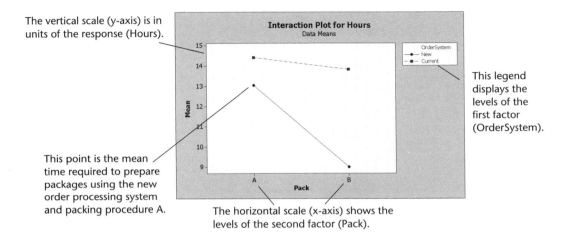

This legend displays the levels of the first factor (OrderSystem).

This point is the mean time required to prepare packages using the new order processing system and packing procedure A.

The horizontal scale (x-axis) shows the levels of the second factor (Pack).

An interaction plot shows the impact that changing the settings of one factor has on another factor. Because an interaction can magnify or diminish main effects, evaluating interactions is extremely important.

The plot shows that book orders processed with the new order processing system and packing procedure B took the fewest hours to prepare (about 9 hours). Orders processed with the current order processing system and packing procedure A took the longest to prepare (about 14.5 hours). Because the slope of the line for the new order processing system is steeper, you conclude that the packing procedure has a greater effect when the new order processing system is used versus the current order processing system.

Based on the results of the experiment, you recommend that the Western shipping center use the new order processing system and packing procedure B to speed up the book shipping process.

Save Project   **1** Choose **File ➤ Save Project As**.

2 Navigate to the folder in which you want to save your files.

3 In **File name**, enter MY_DOE.MPJ.

4 Click **Save**.

packing procedure B. In the next chapter, you learn how to use command language and create and run Execs to quickly rerun an analysis when new data are collected.

6

Using Session Commands

Objectives

In this chapter, you:

- Enable and type session commands, page 6-2
- Conduct an analysis using session commands, page 6-3
- Rerun a series of session commands with Command Line Editor, page 6-5
- Create and run an Exec, page 6-7

Overview

Each menu command has a corresponding session command. Session commands consist of a main command and, in most cases, one or more subcommands. Commands are usually easy-to-remember words, such as PLOT, CHART, or SORT. Both main commands and subcommands can be followed by a series of arguments, which can be columns, constants, or matrices, text strings, or numbers.

Session commands can be:

- Typed into the Session window or the Command Line Editor.
- Copied from the History folder to the Command Line Editor. (When you use menu commands, Minitab generates and stores the corresponding session commands in the History folder.)
- Copied and saved in a file called an Exec, which can be reexecuted and shared with others or used in future sessions.

Use session commands to quickly rerun an analysis in current or future sessions or as an alternative to menu commands. Some users find session commands quicker to use than menu commands once they become familiar with them.

The Western shipping center continuously collects and analyzes shipping time when new data are available. In Chapter 4, *Assessing Quality*, you conducted a capability analysis on data from March. In this chapter, you conduct a capability analysis on data from April using session commands.

To learn more about session commands, choose **Help ➤ Help**, then click **Session Commands** under **References**.

Enabling and Typing Commands

One way to use session commands is to directly type the commands and subcommands at the command prompt in the Session window. However, Minitab does not display the command prompt by default. To enter commands directly into the Session window, you must enable this prompt.

Enable session commands

1 If continuing from the previous chapter, choose **File ➤ New**, then choose **Minitab Project** and click **OK**. Otherwise, just start Minitab.

2 Choose **File ➤ Open Worksheet**.

3 Click **Look in Minitab Sample Data folder**, near the bottom of the dialog box.

4 In the Sample Data folder, double-click Meet Minitab, then choose SESSIONCOMMANDS.MTW. Click **Open**.

5 Click the Session window to make it active.

6 Choose **Editor ➤ Enable Commands**. A check appears next to the menu item.

To change the default options and enable session commands for all future sessions:
1 Choose **Tools ➤ Options ➤ Session Window ➤ Submitting Commands**.
2 Under **Command Language**, click **Enable**.

**Examine
Session
window**

With the command prompt enabled, you can now type session commands in the Session window.

Command
prompt

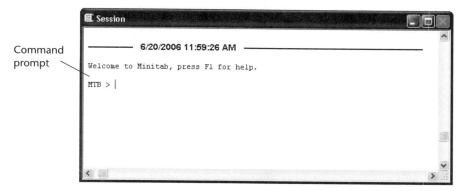

 When you execute a command from a menu and session commands are enabled, the corresponding session command appears in the Session window along with your text output. This technique provides a convenient way to learn session commands.

**Conduct an
analysis with
session
commands**

In Chapter 4, *Assessing Quality*, you conducted a capability analysis to determine whether shipping times were within specifications (less than six delivery days). To perform this analysis, you used **Stat ➤ Quality Tools ➤ Capability Analysis ➤ Normal**. Then, using two different dialog boxes, you entered several variables and values.

To continue evaluating shipping times at the Western shipping center, you plan to repeat this analysis at regular intervals. When you collect new data, you can re-create this chart using just a few session commands, instead of filling out multiple dialog boxes. Analyze the April shipping data using session commands.

1 In the Session window, at the MTB >prompt, type:

CAPABILITY 'Days' 'Date';

2 Press Enter.

The semicolon indicates that you want to type a subcommand.

Notice that the MTB >prompt becomes SUBC>, allowing you to add subcommands for the various options used in the earlier capability analysis.

Subcommand prompt ———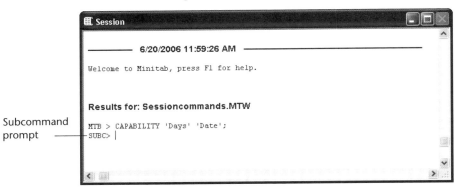

3 At the SUBC> prompt, type:

   USPEC 6;

4 Press [Enter].

5 At the SUBC> prompt, type:

   TARGET 3.33.

6 Press [Enter].

   The period indicates the end of a command sequence.

Minitab displays the capability analysis for the April shipping data.

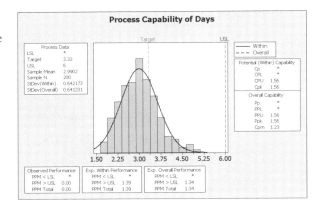

 For more information on session commands, including command and subcommand syntax, type *Help* at the command prompt followed by the first four letters of the command name. For general information on syntax notation, go to **Help ➤ Help**, then click **Session Commands** under **References**. Go to *Notation for session commands* in the Session Command Help index.

Rerunning a Series of Commands

Minitab generates corresponding session commands for most of the menu commands you used, and stores them in the Project Manager's History folder. Rather than repeat all the previous steps of your analysis using the menus, you can simply rerun these commands by selecting them in the History folder and choosing **Edit ➤ Command Line Editor**.

Session commands for the capability analysis you just conducted are stored in the History folder. Use the History folder and the Command Line Editor to re-create the capability analysis.

Open History folder

1 Choose **Window ➤ Project Manager**.

2 Click the **History** folder.

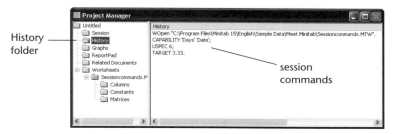

The right pane of the Project Manager contains all the session commands generated during a Minitab session. These commands are stored regardless of whether the command prompt is enabled.

When you select any portion of the session commands in the History folder, those commands automatically appear in the Command Line Editor when you open it.

Reexecute a series of commands

1 To highlight the capability analysis session commands, click *CAPABILITY 'Days' 'Date'*; then press ⟨Shift⟩ and click *TARGET 3.33*.

2 Choose **Edit ➤ Command Line Editor**.

3 Click **Submit Commands**.

Graph window output

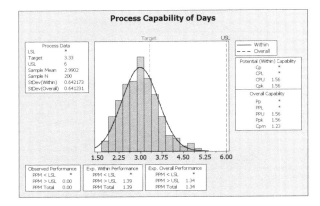

You have re-created the capability analysis in just a few simple steps.

  If you edit a graph or a control chart, Minitab does not automatically generate session commands for the changes made. However, you can generate the session commands, including all editing changes, by using:

■ **Editor ➤ Copy Command Language,** which copies the commands to the clipboard.

■ **Editor ➤ Duplicate Graph,** which re-creates the graph and stores the session commands in the History folder.

For more information on **Copy Command Language** and **Duplicate Graph**, go to *Editor menu* and choose the *Graph window* subentry in the Minitab Help index.

Repeating Analyses with Execs

An Exec is a text file containing a series of Minitab commands. To repeat an analysis without using menu commands or typing session commands, save the commands as an Exec and then run the Exec.

The commands stored in the History folder that you used to rerun the above series of commands with the **Command Line Editor** can also be saved as an Exec and executed at any time.

 For more information about Execs and other more complex macros, choose **Help ➤ Help**, then click **Macros** under **References**.

Create an Exec from the History folder

Save the capability analysis session commands as an Exec. You can use this Exec to continuously analyze the shipping data.

1 Choose **Window ➤ Project Manager**.

2 Click the **History** folder.

3 To select the capability analysis session commands, click *CAPABILITY 'Days' 'Date';*, then press (Shift) and click *TARGET 3.33*.

4 Right-click the selected text and choose **Save As**.

5 Navigate to the folder in which you want to save your files.

6 In **File name**, type *SHIPPINGGRAPHS*.

7 In **Save as type**, choose **Exec Files (∗.MTB)**. Click **Save**.

Reexecute commands

You can repeat this analysis at any time by running the Exec.

1 Choose **File ➤ Other Files ➤ Run an Exec**.

2 Click **Select File**.

3 Select the file SHIPPINGGRAPHS.MTB, then click **Open**.

Graph window output

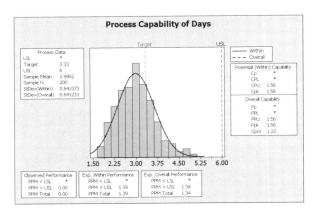

Minitab executes the commands in the Exec to generate the capability analysis. Because you can run the Exec using any worksheet (as long as the column names match), you can share this file with other Minitab users who need to do the same analysis. For example, the Western shipping center may want to share the capability analysis Exec with the Central and Eastern shipping centers so they can conduct the same analysis on their own shipping data. If you want to use the Exec with a different worksheet or with different column, edit the Exec using a text editor such as Notepad.

Save project   Save all of your work in a Minitab project.

1   Choose **File ➤ Save Project As**.

2   In **File name**, type *MY_SESSIONCOMMANDS.MPJ*.

3   Click **Save**.

What Next

You learned how to use session commands as an alternative to menu commands and as a way to quickly rerun an analysis. In the next chapter, you create a report to show the results of your analysis to your colleagues.

7

Generating a Report

Objectives

In this chapter, you:

- Add a graph to the ReportPad, page 7-2
- Add Session window output to the ReportPad, page 7-3
- Edit in the ReportPad, page 7-5
- Save and view a report, page 7-6
- Copy the ReportPad contents to a word processor, page 7-7
- Edit a Minitab graph in another application, page 7-7

Overview

Minitab has several tools to help you create reports:

- ReportPad in the Project Manager, to which you can add Minitab-generated results throughout your sessions
- Copy to Word Processor, which enables you to easily copy content from the ReportPad to a word processor
- Embedded Graph Editor, for editing graphs with Minitab after you have copied them to other applications

To show your colleagues the shipping data analysis results, you want to prepare a report that includes various elements from your Minitab sessions.

Using the ReportPad

Throughout *Meet Minitab*, you performed several analyses and you want to share the results with colleagues. Minitab's Project Manager contains a folder, called the ReportPad, in which you can create simple reports.

The ReportPad acts as a simple text editor (like Notepad), from which you can quickly print or save in RTF (rich text) or HTML (Web) format. In ReportPad, you can:

- Store Minitab results and graphs in a single document
- Add comments and headings
- Rearrange your output
- Change font sizes
- Print entire output from an analysis
- Create Web-ready reports

Add graph to ReportPad

You can add components to ReportPad by right-clicking on a graph or Session window output, then choosing **Append to Report**. In addition, text and graphs from other applications can be copied and pasted into Minitab's ReportPad.

Add the histogram with fits and groups you created in Chapter 2, *Graphing Data*, to the ReportPad.

1 If continuing from the previous chapter, choose **File ➤ New**, then choose **Minitab Project**. Click **OK**. Otherwise, just start Minitab.

2 Choose **File ➤ Open Project**.

3 Navigate to C:\Program Files\Minitab 15\English\Sample Data\Meet Minitab. (Adjust this if you chose to install Minitab to a location other than the default.)

4 Choose REPORTS.MPJ. Click **Open**.

5 Choose **Window ➤ Histogram of Days**.

6 Right-click anywhere in the graph region, then choose **Append Graph to Report**.

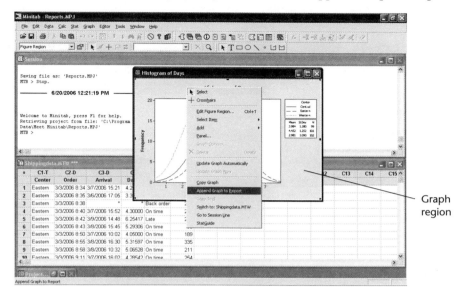

Graph
region

7 Choose **Window ➤ Project Manager**.

8 Click the **ReportPad** folder. The histogram has been added to the ReportPad.

Add Session window output to ReportPad

You also can add Session window output to the ReportPad. In Chapter 3, *Analyzing Data*, you displayed descriptive statistics for the three regional shipping centers. Add the output for the three centers to the ReportPad.

1 Choose **Window ➤ Session**.

2 In the Session window, click in the output for *Results for Center = Central*. Then right-click and choose **Append Section to Report**. The section of output Minitab appends is delineated by the output titles (which are in bold text).

If you right-click in this area and choose **Append Section to Report**, the results for the Central shipping center are added to the ReportPad.

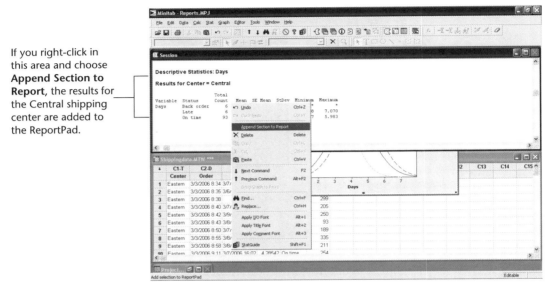

3 Repeat the steps above for the *Results for Center = Eastern* and *Results for Center = Western*.

4 Choose **Window ➤ Project Manager**, then click the **ReportPad** folder. Click 🔲 to maximize the window to see more of your report.

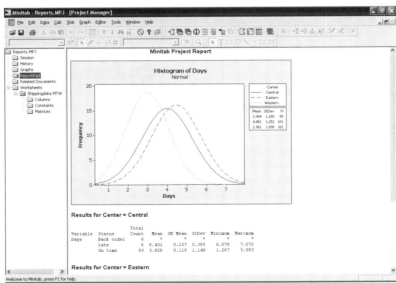

To simultaneously add multiple sections of Session window output to the ReportPad:
1   Highlight the Session window output.
2   Right-click in the Session window.
3   Choose **Append Selected Lines to Report**.

Edit in ReportPad

Customize the report by replacing the default title and adding a short comment to the graphical output.

1   Highlight the default title (**Minitab Project Report**). Type *Report on Shipping Data*. Press (Enter).

2   Below *Report on Shipping Data*, type *Histogram of delivery time by center*.

3   Highlight the text *Histogram of delivery time by center*. Right-click the highlighted text and choose **Font**.

4   From **Font**, choose **Arial**. From **Font style**, choose **Regular**. From **Size**, choose **11**. From **Color**, choose **Maroon**.

5   Click **OK**.

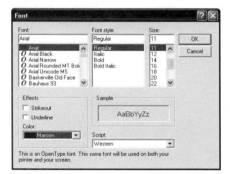

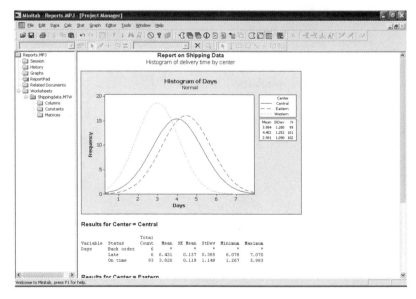

You now have a simple report that illustrates some of your results. If you save a Minitab project, you can add additional comments and formatting at any time because Minitab saves the ReportPad contents as part of the project.

> All graphs and Session window output remain fully editable after they are appended to the ReportPad. To edit a graph in the ReportPad, double-click the graph to activate Minitab's embedded graph editing tools.

Saving a Report

You can save the contents of the ReportPad (as well as Session window output and worksheets) either as Rich Text Format (RTF) or Web Page (HTML) so you can open them in other applications.

Save as RTF file

Save your report as an RTF file to send electronically to colleagues or to open in other applications.

1 In the Project Manager, right-click the **ReportPad** folder and choose **Save Report As**.

2 Navigate to the folder in which you want to save your files.

3 In **File name,** type *ShippingReport*.

4 In **Save as type**, choose **Rich Text Format** (*.RTF). Click **Save**.

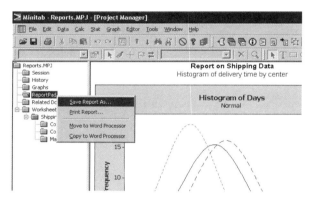

Copying a Report to a Word Processor

Word processors provide formatting options not available in ReportPad, such as adding callouts to highlight important findings and laying graphs side by side.

Two tools in ReportPad, Move to Word Processor and Copy to Word Processor, enable you to transfer the contents of the ReportPad to your word processor without copying and pasting:

■ Copy to Word Processor transfers the ReportPad contents into a word processor while leaving the original contents in the ReportPad.

Copy report to a word processor

1 In the Project Manager, right-click the **ReportPad** folder.

2 Choose **Copy to Word Processor**.

3 In **File name**, type *Shipping Report*. You do not need to choose a file type, because Rich Text Format (*.RTF) is the only option available.

4 Click **Save**.

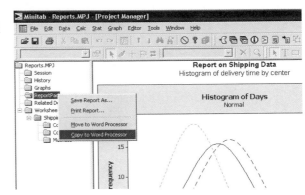

Minitab automatically opens your default word processor and loads the RTF file you just saved.

You can now edit your Minitab content in the word processor.

Using Embedded Graph Editing Tools

When you copy graphs to a word processor or other application, either with copy/paste or with Copy to Word Processor, you can use the Embedded Graph Editor to access all Minitab's graph editing tools.

Edit Minitab graph in a word processor

To blend the graph into the report background and create a better visual effect, use the Embedded Graph Editor tools to change the fill pattern, borders, and fill lines of the graph without returning to Minitab.

1 In the word processor, double-click the histogram. Notice that you now have several toolbars with editing tools.

Minitab
graph editing
tools

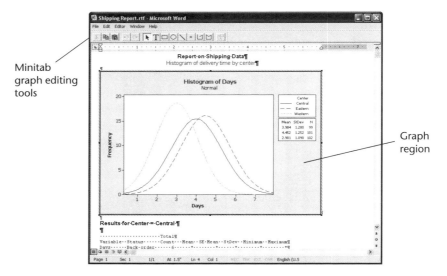

Graph
region

The graph is in edit mode; you can double-click a graph item to edit it as you would in Minitab.

2 Double-click in the graph region of the histogram.

3 Under **Fill Pattern**, choose **Custom**.

4 From **Type**, choose ⌐N⌐.

5 Under **Borders and Fill Lines**, choose **Custom**.

6 From **Type**, choose **None**. Click **OK**.

7 Click outside of the graph to end edit mode.

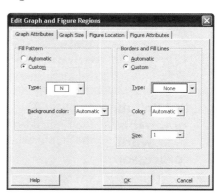

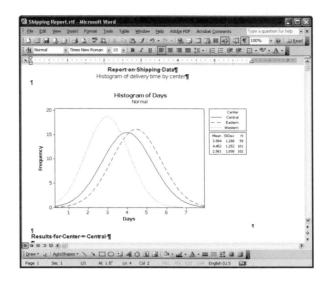

 For more information about Minitab's Embedded Graph Editor, go to *Embedded graph editor* in the Minitab Help index.

Save project   Save all of your work in a Minitab project.

1   In Minitab, Choose **File ➤ Save Project As**.

2   In **File name**, type *MY_REPORTS.MPJ*.

3   Click **Save**.

What Next

In the next chapter, you learn to prepare a Minitab worksheet. You combine data from multiple sources and place them in Minitab. Also, to prepare the data and simplify the analysis, you edit the data and reorganize columns and rows.

8

Preparing a Worksheet

Objectives

In this chapter, you:

- Open a worksheet, page 8-2

- Merge data from an Excel spreadsheet into a Minitab worksheet, page 8-3

- Merge data from a text file into a worksheet, page 8-4

- View worksheet information, page 8-5

- Replace missing value, page 8-6

- Stack columns of data, page 8-6

- Code data, page 8-8

- Add column names, page 8-8

- Insert and name a new data column, page 8-8

- Use the Calculator to assign a formula to a column, page 8-9

Overview

In many cases, you use worksheets that were already set up for you, as you have throughout *Meet Minitab*. Sometimes, however, you must combine data from different sources and place them in a Minitab worksheet before beginning an analysis. Minitab can use data from:

- Previously saved Minitab worksheet files

- Text files

■ Microsoft Excel documents

To place these data in Minitab, you can:

■ Type directly into Minitab

■ Copy and paste from other applications

■ Open from a variety of file types, including Excel or text files

After your data are in Minitab, you may need to edit cells and reorganize columns and rows to get the data ready for analysis. Common manipulations include stacking, subsetting, specifying column names, and editing data values.

This chapter shows how to place data from different sources into Minitab and how SHIPPINGDATA.MTW, used in chapters 2 and 3, was prepared for analysis.

Getting Data from Different Sources

For the initial *Meet Minitab* analyses, the worksheet SHIPPINGDATA.MTW, which contains data from three shipping centers, was already set up. However, the three shipping centers originally stored the book order data in different ways:

■ Eastern—in a Minitab worksheet

■ Central—in a Microsoft Excel file

■ Western—in a text file

To analyze all the book order data, you must combine the data from all three shipping centers into a single Minitab worksheet.

Open a worksheet

Begin with data from the Eastern shipping center, which are stored in a Minitab worksheet called EASTERN.MTW.

1 If continuing from the previous chapter, choose **File ➤ New**, then choose **Minitab Project** and click **OK**. Otherwise, just start Minitab.

2 Choose **File ➤ Open Worksheet**.

3 Click **Look in Minitab Sample Data folder**, near the bottom of the dialog box.

4 In the Sample Data folder, double-click Meet Minitab, then choose EASTERN.MTW. Click **Open**.

 Minitab can open a variety of file types. To see the file types, click **Files of type** in the Open Worksheet dialog box.

Merge data from Excel

The Central shipping center stored data in an Excel spreadsheet.

To combine the Central book order data with the Eastern data, merge the data in the Excel spreadsheet with the data in the current Minitab worksheet.

1 Choose **File ➤ Open Worksheet**.

2 From **Files of type**, choose **Excel (∗.xls)**.

3 Choose CENTRAL.XLS.

4 Choose **Merge**.

5 Click **Open**.

Examine worksheet

Choosing **Merge** adds the Excel data to your current worksheet. Minitab places the data in cells to the right of the current worksheet data in columns C5–C8. If you had not chosen **Merge**, Minitab would have placed the data in a separate worksheet.

Original data   Merged data

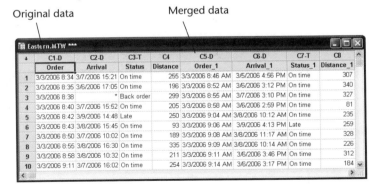

Minitab also provides a Merge Worksheets menu command that provides additional options to merge two or more open worksheets. For more information on Merge, go to *Merge Worksheets* in the Minitab Help index.

Merge data from a text file

The Western shipping center stored data in a simple text file that you can open using Notepad or WordPad. To combine the Western book order data with the Eastern and Central data, merge the data in the text file with the data in the current Minitab worksheet.

1 Choose **File ➤ Open Worksheet**.

2 From **Files of type**, choose **Text (*.txt)**.

3 Choose WESTERN.TXT.

4 Choose **Merge**.

5 Click **Open**.

Examine worksheet

Choosing **Merge** adds the data from the text file to the current worksheet. Minitab places the data in cells to the right of the current worksheet data in columns C9–C12. If you had not chosen **Merge**, Minitab would have placed the data in a separate worksheet,

Original data   Merged data

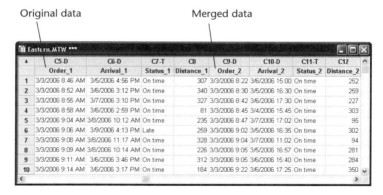

Before opening a text file in Minitab, you can see what the data will look like in the worksheet by choosing **Preview** in the Open Worksheet dialog box.

 Not all text files are not in a format that can be easily imported. Minitab provides several tools for interpreting text file formats. For more information, go to *Text files* in the Minitab Help index.

Preparing the Worksheet for Analysis

With the data in a single worksheet, you are almost ready to begin the analysis. However, you must modify the worksheet by:

- Replacing a missing value

- Stacking data

- Replacing data

- Adding column names

- Adding a new column

- Creating a column of calculated values

 For a complete list of data manipulations available in Minitab, go to *Data menu* in the Minitab Help index.

Show worksheet information

To view a summary of your worksheet columns, use on the Project Manager toolbar. This button will open the Project Manager's Columns subfolder in the Worksheets folder. This summary is especially useful in identifying unequal column lengths or columns that contain missing values.

1 Click on the Project Manager toolbar or press Ctrl + Alt + I.

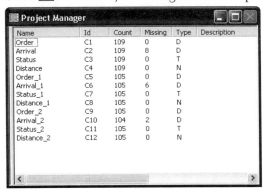

The Columns subfolder contains details on the current worksheet. Within each center, the count should be the same for all columns. Notice that the counts for the Eastern data (C1–C4) are 109 for all columns, and the counts for the Central data (C5–C8) are 105 for all columns. However, for the Western center, C10 has a count of 104 unlike the other columns, which have a count of 105.

2 Click again to return to your previous view.

 For more information on the Project Manager toolbar, go to *Project Manager Toolbar* in the Minitab Help index.

Examine worksheet

Examine C10 to see what value is missing. Notice that the last row of the column is empty. When you copy and paste data from a text or Excel file into a worksheet, Minitab interprets empty numeric or data/time cells as missing values, which appear as asterisks (∗) by default. However, if the last row of a column of data in a text file contains an empty cell, Minitab

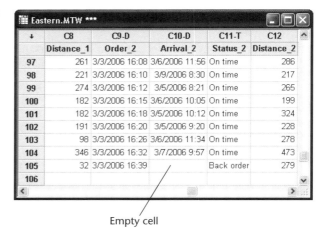

Empty cell

leaves the cell empty when you paste the data into the worksheet, as you can see in column C10.

Replace missing value

For Minitab to perform the correct analysis, you must type the missing value symbol in the empty cell of the last row.

1　Click the Data window to make it active, then choose **Editor ➤ Go To**....

2　In **Enter column number or name**, type *C10*.

3　In **Enter row number**, type *105*. Click **OK**.

4　In row 105 of column C10, type an asterisk (∗). Press (Enter).

Stack data

Now that the data are assembled in a single Minitab worksheet, notice the similar variables for each shipping center. Some Minitab commands allow data from different groups to remain unstacked in separate columns. Others require groups to be stacked, with a column of group levels. However, all analyses can be performed with stacked data.

To analyze the data, you need to rearrange these variables into stacked columns. You can move data within the worksheet by copying and pasting or use Data menu items to rearrange blocks of data.

1 Choose **Data ➤ Stack ➤ Blocks of Columns**.

2 From the list of variables, highlight *Order*, *Arrival*, *Status*, and *Distance*. Click **Select** to move the variables into the first row of **Stack two or more blocks of columns on top of each other**. Move to the next row.

3 Repeat step 2 for the order, arrival, status, and distance columns for the Central and Western shipping centers.

4 Under **Store stacked data in**, choose **New worksheet**. In **Name**, type *MY_SHIPPINGDATA*.

5 Check **Use variable names in subscript column**.

6 Click **OK**.

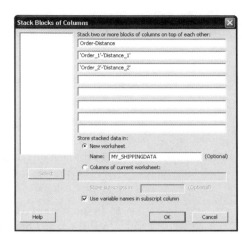

Examine worksheet

The variables for the shipping centers are all in the same columns, with Order (Eastern center), Order_1 (Central center), and Order_2 (Western center) acting as labels or subscripts to indicate from which shipping center the data originated.

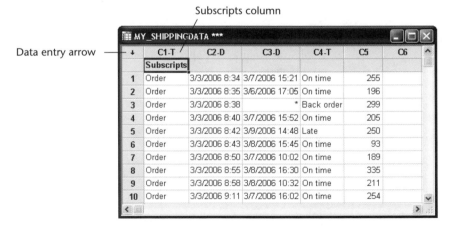

Code data   The labels in the Subscripts column do not adequately indicate which center the data are from. Code the labels with more meaningful names.

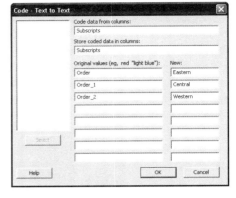

1 Choose **Data ➤ Code ➤ Text to Text**.

2 In **Code data from columns**, enter *Subscripts*.

3 In **Store coded data in columns**, enter *Subscripts*.

4 In the first row under **Original values**, type *Order*. In the first row under **New**, type *Eastern*.

5 In the second row under **Original values**, type *Order_1*. In the second row under **New**, type *Central*.

6 In the third row under **Original values**, type *Order_2*. In the third row under **New**, type *Western*.

7 Click **OK**.

The shipping center labels in the subscripts column are now Eastern, Central, and Western.

Add column names   Add column names to the stacked data.

1 Click the data entry arrow in the upper left corner of the Data window to make it point to the right.

2 Click in the name cell of **C1**. To replace the label *Subscripts*, type *Center*, then press ⟨Enter⟩.

3 Repeat for the rest of the names:

- In **C2**, type *Order*.

- In **C3**, type *Arrival*.

- In **C4**, type *Status*.

- In **C5**, type *Distance*.

Calculate difference values   Before saving your new worksheet and performing analyses, you need to calculate the number of days that elapsed between order and delivery dates. You can use Minitab's Calculator to assign a formula to a column that calculates these values. If you change or add data, the calculated values will update automatically.

Insert and name a column

Insert a column named *Days* between *Arrival* and *Status*.

1   Click any cell in C4 to make it active.

2   Right-click and choose **Insert Columns**.

3   Click in the name cell of C4. Type *Days*, then press Enter.

Use Calculator to assign a formula to a column

Use Minitab's Calculator to perform basic arithmetic or mathematical functions. Minitab stores the results in a column or constant. You can assign the formula to the column so the calculated values update automatically if the data change.

Compute the delivery time and store the values in the Days column.

1   Choose **Calc ➤ Calculator**.

2   In **Store result in variable**, enter *Days*.

3   In **Expression**, enter *Arrival – Order*.

4   Check **Assign as a formula**.

5   Click **OK**.

 For more information on formulas in columns, go to *Formulas* in the Minitab Help index. For more information on Minitab's Calculator and the available operations and functions, go to *Calculator* in the Minitab Help index.

 You can also add a formula to a column by selecting the column and choosing **Editor ➤ Formulas ➤ Assign Formula To Column**.

Examine worksheet

The Days column contains the newly calculated values that represent delivery time. These values are expressed in numbers of days. When you assign a formula to a column, an indicator appears in the upper right corner of the column heading on the worksheet. This indicator tells you whether the formula is properly defined and whether the data need to be updated by re-calculating the values. The green plus sign ▦ indicates the data are up-to-date.

Status indicator

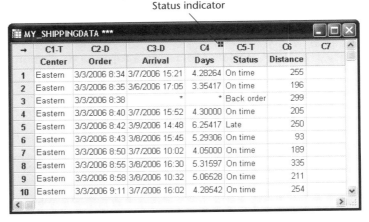

> Place your cursor over the status indicator to view the formula assigned to the column. Double-click the status indicator to edit the formula.

Update worksheet

Suppose you learn that the arrival date for a shipment in the Central shipping center is incorrect. You can correct the date in the worksheet and Minitab will automatically update the Days column.

Update the arrival date in row 127 from 3/6/2006 to 3/7/2006.

1 In row 127 of the worksheet, edit the day in the date in the Arrival column by double-clicking the cell to put it in edit mode. Change 3/6/2006 to 3/7/2006.

2 Press [Enter].

Examine worksheet

Minitab automatically updates the value in the Days column from 2.98125 to 3.98125.

Original worksheet   Updated worksheet

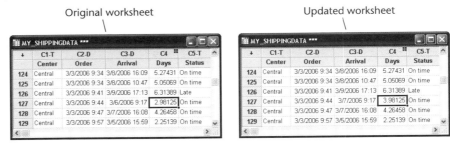

> You can also choose to update the calculated values manually. First, choose **Editor ➤ Formulas ➤ Calculate All Formulas Automatically** to uncheck this option. When the status indicator is yellow, indicating formulas are out of date, you can choose **Editor ➤ Formulas ➤ Calculate All Formulas Now** to update all formulas in the project. This command is active only if formulas are out of date and **Calculate All Formulas Automatically** is not checked in the Editor menu.

Save
worksheet

Save all of your work in a Minitab worksheet.

1 Choose **File ➤ Save Current Worksheet As**.

2 Navigate to the folder in which you want to save your files.

3 In **File name**, type *MY_SHIPPINGDATA*.

4 From **Save as type**, choose **Minitab**.

5 Click **Save**.

What Next

The shipping center data from several sources are in Minitab and are set up properly for analysis. In the next chapter, you adjust the Minitab defaults to expedite future shipping data analyses.

9
Customizing Minitab

Objectives

In this chapter, you:

- Change default options for graphs, page 9-2

- Create a new toolbar, page 9-3

- Add commands to a custom toolbar, page 9-4

- Assign shortcut keys for a menu command, page 9-5

- Restore your Minitab default settings using Manage Profiles, page 9-7

Overview

Minitab has several tools for changing default options or creating custom tools such as individualized toolbars or keyboard shortcuts.

Use **Tools ➤ Options** to change defaults for:

- Program settings (memory usage, initial directory, window layout, and dialog box)

- Data and Session windows

- Statistical commands

- Graphs

Use **Tools ➤ Customize** to:

- Assign a shortcut key to a menu item

- Set options for how Minitab displays toolbars

- Create custom icons for menu items or toolbar buttons

Now that you have completed your first book shipment analysis and generated a report, you decide to use **Tools ➤ Options** and **Tools ➤ Customize** to tailor the Minitab environment to make future analyses quicker and easier.

Setting Options

You can change many options during a Minitab session, such as changing graph display settings or enabling the session command prompt. However, when you exit Minitab, these options revert back to the defaults for future Minitab sessions.

If you want a setting to be your default for all Minitab sessions, use **Tools ➤ Options**. Settings that you change remain active until you change them again.

Because you are planning to do similar analyses on the shipping data during the next few months, you want to change your default preferences.

 If you change options, you can restore Minitab's default settings at any time. For more information, see *Restoring Minitab's Default Settings* on page 9-6.

Add automatic footnote

Because you will create the same graphs with similar data in the future, you need a way to distinguish the results of each analysis. You decide to add an automatic footnote to your graphs to include the worksheet name, last modification date, and some information on the data used.

1 If continuing from the previous chapter, choose **File ➤ New**, then choose **Minitab Project** and click **OK**. Otherwise, just start Minitab.

2 Choose **File ➤ Open Worksheet**.

3 Click **Look in Minitab Sample Data folder**, near the bottom of the dialog box.

4 In the Sample Data folder, double-click Meet Minitab, then choose SHIPPINGDATA.MTW. Click **Open**.

5 Choose **Tools ➤ Options ➤ Graphics ➤ Annotation ➤ My Footnote**.

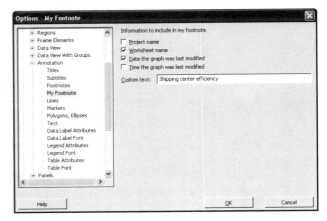

6 Under **Information to include in my footnote**, check **Worksheet name** and **Date the graph was last modified**.

7 In **Custom text**, type *Shipping center efficiency*. Click **OK**.

With these settings, every time you create a graph, Minitab adds the automatic footnote.

Create a histogram to view footnote

To see an example of the automatic footnote, create a histogram.

1 Choose **Graph ➤ Histogram**.

2 Choose **With Fit and Groups**, then click **OK**.

3 In **Graph variables**, enter *Days*.

4 In **Categorical variables for grouping (0-3)**, enter *Center*.

5 Click **OK**.

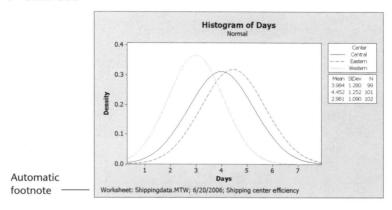

Automatic footnote ——— Worksheet: Shippingdata.MTW; 6/20/2006; Shipping center efficiency

Creating a Custom Toolbar

In addition to saving time by changing the default options settings for individual commands, you also can save time in future Minitab sessions by using **Tools ➤ Customize**.

Use **Customize** to create new menus and toolbars that contain only the commands you choose to add, and to assign keyboard shortcuts to commands that you access frequently.

Create a toolbar

During some analyses, you return to the same menu items many times. Combining these items on a single custom toolbar can simplify future analysis.

Create a custom toolbar that includes some of the commands used in the shipping center analysis.

1 Choose **Tools ➤ Customize**.

2 Click the **Toolbars** tab.

3 Click **New**.

4 In **Toolbar Name**, type *Shipping Data*. Click **OK**.

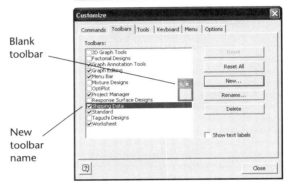

A new blank toolbar labeled *Shipping Data* appears under **Toolbars**, and the new toolbar name appears in the toolbar list.

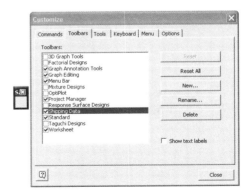

Add commands to the toolbar

Add commands to the blank toolbar. In the shipping center analysis, you used **Graph ➤ Histogram** and **Graph ➤ Scatterplot**, so you want to add these commands to a toolbar.

1 Click and drag the blank toolbar off the Customize dialog box.

2 Click the **Commands** tab.

3 Under **Categories**, choose **Graph**.

4 Under **Commands**, choose **Histogram**.

Under **Categories** is a list of all Minitab menus. When you select one of these menus, a list of corresponding menu items appears under **Commands**.

5 Click and drag **Histogram** to the new toolbar.

6 Under **Commands**, choose **Scatterplot**.

7 Click and drag **Scatterplot** to the new toolbar.

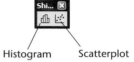

Histogram   Scatterplot

8 Click **Close**.

You can add any number of commands until you have a custom toolbar that includes all your frequently used commands. To access the new toolbar items quickly from the keyboard, assign keyboard shortcuts.

 You also can create a custom menu. For more information on **Tools ➤ Customize**, go to *Customize* in the Minitab Help index.

Assigning Shortcut Keys

Minitab already contains many shortcut keys for frequently used functions such as Copy ($\boxed{\text{Ctrl}}$+$\boxed{\text{C}}$), Paste ($\boxed{\text{Ctrl}}$+$\boxed{\text{V}}$), and Save As ($\boxed{\text{Ctrl}}$+$\boxed{\text{S}}$). Shortcut keys enable you to quickly bypass the menus and open dialog boxes.

To assign shortcut keys, use **Tools ➤ Customize ➤ Keyboard**.

Assign a shortcut key

Because you often create histograms for your shipping data analysis, you want to assign a shortcut key for this command.

1 Choose **Tools ➤ Customize**.

2 Click the **Keyboard** tab.

3 From **Category**, choose **Graph**.

   Categories provides a list of all Minitab menus. When you select one of these menus, a list of corresponding menu items appears under **Commands**.

4 Under **Commands**, choose **Histogram**.

5 Click in **Press New Shortcut Key**.

6 Press Ctrl+Shift+H.

   Under **Press New Shortcut Key**, the **Assigned to** text displays the current status of the selected key combination. In this case, the text reads [**Unassigned**]. Keys or key combinations that are already assigned to a command are indicated here. Any existing combination that conflicts with your choice must be removed from its command before it can be assigned to a new command.

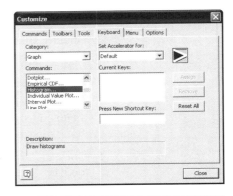

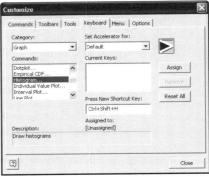

7 Click **Assign**. The new shortcut key appears under **Current Keys**.

8 Click **Close**.

You can now access the Histogram gallery by pressing Ctrl+Shift+H.

  For a list of Minitab's default shortcut keys, see the back cover of this book, choose **Help ➤ Keyboard Map,** or go to *Shortcut keys* in the Minitab Help index.

Restoring Minitab's Default Settings

Any settings you change using **Tools ➤ Options** and **Tools ➤ Customize**, as well as any changes you have made to date/time data settings or value order settings, are stored in a profile. You can activate and deactivate this profile (and remove all these settings) using **Tools ➤ Manage Profiles**. You also can export and share this profile with other users who are doing a similar analysis.

All settings that you have adjusted while working through *Meet Minitab* are already stored in your active profile. Deactivate the current profile to restore Minitab's default settings and change the name of the profile to use for future shipping center analyses.

 For more information on managing profiles, go to *Manage Profiles* in the Minitab Help index.

Restore defaults

1 Choose **Tools ➤ Manage Profiles**.

2 Click ◄ to move *MyProfile* from **Active profiles** to **Available profiles**.

3 Double-click *MyProfile* in **Available profiles**, then type *ShippingCenterAnalysis*.

4 Click **OK**.

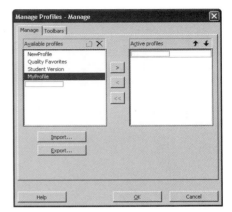

The default settings are now restored. Minitab creates a new active profile to store any changes you make after this point.

To activate the settings you adjusted during your *Meet Minitab* sessions, move the current active profile to **Available profiles**, move *ShippingCenterAnalysis* to **Active profiles**, then click **OK**.

 You also can reset Minitab's defaults by double-clicking the shortcut named *RestoreMinitabDefaults English* located in the English folder under the main Minitab 15 folder installed on your hard drive. Export any profiles you want to keep before running this program.

Save project

Save all of your work in a Minitab project.

1 Choose **File ➤ Save Project As**.

2 Navigate to the folder in which you want to save your files.

3 In **File name**, type *MY_CUSTOMIZE.MPJ*.

4 Click **Save**.

What Next

Your analysis is complete, but what do you do if you have questions or want more information about a topic? The next chapter suggests ways to get answers to your Minitab questions and provides details about how to use Minitab Help and StatGuide.

10

Getting Help

Objectives

In this chapter, you:

- Get answers and find information, page 10-2
- Use Minitab Help, page 10-6
- Use Minitab StatGuide, page 10-8
- Use Session Command Help, page 10-10

Overview

If you find yourself with unanswered questions or discover that you need more details about a topic, Minitab can help.

From assistance with completing a dialog box, to guidance for statistical interpretations, to instructions for using session commands in your analysis, Minitab's easy-to-use online documentation and Internet resources can help you find the answers you need.

This chapter discusses using Help, StatGuide, and Session Command Help to explore Minitab and suggests ways to find answers to your Minitab questions.

Getting Answers and Information

Meet Minitab focused on only a few of Minitab's commonly used features. For details about other commands, functions, and statistical concepts, explore Minitab's documentation and online resources.

Resource	Description	Access
Help	Documentation on Minitab features and concepts. Includes information on: ■ Menus and dialog boxes ■ Methods and formulas ■ Session commands ■ Macros	■ Click **Help** in any dialog box. ■ Click 🔲 on the toolbar. ■ Press F1 at any time. ■ Choose **Help ➤ Help**. See *Help* on page 10-6 for more information.
Using Help	General information on navigating Minitab Help.	Choose **Help ➤ Help**, then click **Using Help** under **Basics**.
StatGuide	Statistical guidance that focuses on interpretation of sample results.	■ Right-click in the Session window or a Graph window, then choose **StatGuide**. ■ Right-click in the Session or Graph folder of the Project Manager, then choose **StatGuide**. ■ Click 🔲 on the toolbar. ■ Press Shift+F1. ■ Choose **Help ➤ StatGuide**. See *StatGuide* on page 10-8 for more information.
Minitab Statistical Glossary	This comprehensive glossary covers all areas of Minitab statistics. Each definition contains practical, easy-to-understand information.	Choose **Help ➤ Glossary**.
Tutorials	Step-by-step tutorials that introduce the Minitab environment and provide an overview of Minitab.	Choose **Help ➤ Tutorials**.

Resource	Description	Access
Session Command Help	Documentation on Minitab session commands, which you can use interactively or to create a macro.	▪ Choose **Help ➤ Help**, then click **Session Commands** under **References**. ▪ At the MTB > prompt in the Session window, type *HELP.* ▪ To access information on a specific session command, at the MTB > prompt in the Session window, type *HELP* followed by a command. See *Session Command Help* on page 10-10 for more information.
Macros Help	Support for writing and executing Minitab macros, which commands stored in text files.	Choose **Help ➤ Help**, then click **Macros** under **References**.
Meet Minitab PDF	A PDF version of *Meet Minitab.*	From the Start menu, choose **Programs ➤ Minitab Solutions ➤ Minitab Reference ➤ Meet Minitab 15 English**.
What's New	Information about new features in Release 15 of Minitab.	From the Start menu, choose **Programs ➤ Minitab Solutions ➤ Minitab Reference ➤ What's New in Minitab 15 English**.
ReadMe	Late-breaking information on this release of Minitab, including details on changes to the software or documentation.	From the Start menu, choose **Programs ➤ Minitab Solutions ➤ Minitab Reference ➤ ReadMe Minitab 15 English**.
Technical support	Communicate with our highly-skilled technical support specialists; get answers to common technical questions; download macros; and download free software updates of Minitab.	Go to *customer.minitab.com* to contact technical support. You can also call technical support at 1-814-231-2682. For online information, visit *www.minitab.com/support*.
Web site	Learn about our products, training, resources, and more.	Go to *www.minitab.com*.

Please send comments about Minitab's online and print documentation to doc_comments@minitab.com.

Minitab Help Overview

The components of Minitab's online documentation—as well as other related information—are summarized on a single page. From this page, you can proceed to detailed assistance, instructions, and support topics. This overview organizes links to Help topics according to Minitab's menu structure.

Finding information

To display the overview page:

- Choose **Help ➤ Help**.
- Press F1 .
- Click ❓ on the Standard toolbar.

The links provided under the headings shown below make finding information quick and easy:

- **Basics**—how to use Help, guidelines and tutorials for getting started with Minitab, and descriptions of Minitab windows

- **References**—examples of commands, glossary of terms and abbreviations, instructions for using session commands and macros, and the methods and formulas used by Minitab

- **Service and Support**—how to register Minitab, ways to communicate with Technical Support, and descriptions of Minitab's documentation, Internet resources, and other products

Use these links to access basic facts, reference material, and service and support information.

Click a menu link to view Help topics for all commands on that menu.

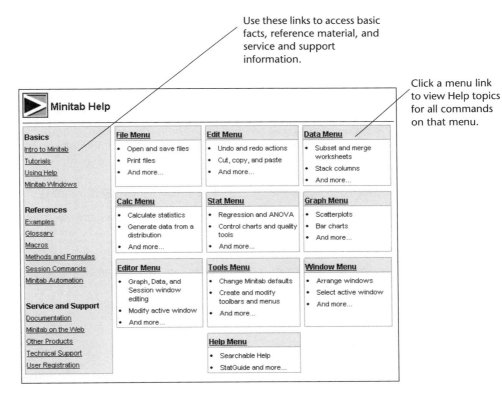

For more information about the Minitab Help environment, choose **Help ➤ Help**, then click **Using Help** under **Basics**.

Help

Minitab Help is a comprehensive, convenient source of information that includes menu and dialog box instructions, overviews, examples, guidance for setting up your data, and methods and formulas. You can explore Minitab's statistical features and discover new methods for routine tasks. Help also provides guidance on using Minitab's statistics, quality control, reliability and survival analysis, and design of experiments tools.

Additionally, in Help, you can learn about the Minitab environment; using session commands; writing macros and Execs; Minitab's input, output, and data manipulation capabilities; and working with data and graphs.

Finding information

Most Help topics appear in a window that consists of three areas:

- **Toolbar**—contains buttons for hiding and showing the navigation pane, returning to a previous topic, printing one or more topics, and tools for working within the Help environment

- **Navigation pane**—provides three tabs for exploring the table of contents and index, and searching for words or phrases

- **Topic pane**—displays the selected Help topic

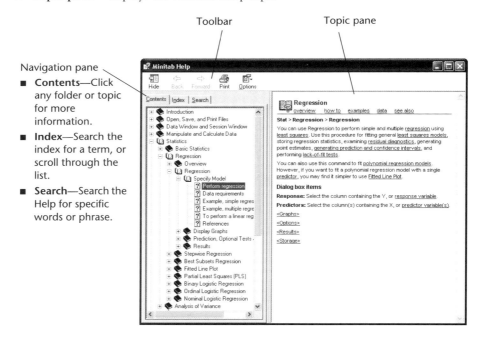

Toolbar · Topic pane

Navigation pane
- **Contents**—Click any folder or topic for more information.
- **Index**—Search the index for a term, or scroll through the list.
- **Search**—Search the Help for specific words or phrase.

Command-specific information

You can access command-specific assistance from within Minitab dialog boxes by clicking **Help** in the dialog box or pressing F1. Help suggests ways to complete the dialog box and encourages a thorough understanding of the task by supplying links to related topics and associated commands.

Most main dialog box topics contain the following links:

- **Overview** of subject area, including information such as why a certain method is useful and how to choose which method to use

- **How to** instructions on completing the dialog box

- **Example** of using the command, including output and interpretation

- **Data** requirements that explain how you should arrange the data in the worksheet and what data types you can analyze with that command

- **See also** links to related topics and commands, including methods and formulas

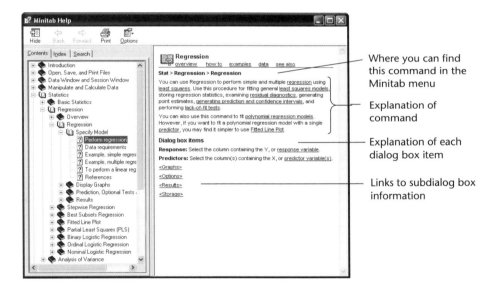

StatGuide

The Minitab StatGuide explains how to interpret statistical tables and graphs in a practical, easy-to-understand way. Unlike Help, which provides guidance for using Minitab, the StatGuide focuses on the interpretation of Minitab results, using preselected examples to explain the output.

StatGuide topics include information such as:

- Real-life data analysis situations

- Brief summaries of statistical capabilities

- Emphasis on important components of the output

Finding information

After you issue a command, you can learn more about the output by examining StatGuide's example output and interpretation. The StatGuide provides a direct path to command-specific guidance:

- Right-click in the Session window output or on a graph, then choose **StatGuide**.

- Click in the Session window output or on a graph, then click 📧 on the toolbar or press Shift+F1.

- In the Project Manager, click the name of the Session window output or graph, then click 📧 on the toolbar or press Shift+F1. You can also right-click the Session window or graph output name, then choose **StatGuide**.

You can also access the StatGuide by choosing **Help ➤ StatGuide**. To locate specific words or phrases, choose **Help ➤ StatGuide**, then click the **Search** tab.

The Minitab StatGuide navigation pane contains:

- **Contents**—Explore the StatGuide. The topics appear in the order of Minitab's Stat menu, followed by Graphs. Double-click a book to access the menu items.

- **Index**—Search the index for a term, or scroll through the list of keywords.

- **Search**—Search the contents of the StatGuide to find all occurrences of a specific word or phrase.

Command-specific information

Each topic in the StatGuide provides interpretation for a part of the Session window output or graph and includes the following sections:

- The first section directly below the main heading contains general guidance on interpreting the output or graph.

- The Example Output section contains the output or graph.

- The Interpretation section contains specific interpretation for the output or graph shown in the topic.

Display a list of all StatGuide topics for a command.

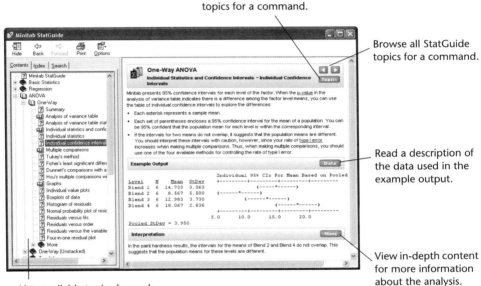

Browse all StatGuide topics for a command.

Read a description of the data used in the example output.

View in-depth content for more information about the analysis.

Lists available topics for each command and shows your location within the StatGuide.

Session Command Help

In addition to using Minitab's menus and dialog boxes, you can also conduct analyses, generate graphs, and manipulate data using session commands. Each Minitab menu command has a corresponding session command, which consists of a main command and, usually, one or more subcommands. Session commands are especially useful because they can be used to create macros, which are session commands stored in a text file. Macros can help automate repeated tasks. See **Help ➤ Help**, then click **Macros** under **References** for more information about how to write Execs and macros.

Finding information

To access Minitab Session Command Help, choose **Help ➤ Help**, then click **Session Commands** under **References**.

The Session Command Help environment is similar to Minitab Help. The toolbar, navigation pane, and topic pane provide the necessary tools for learning and using session commands.

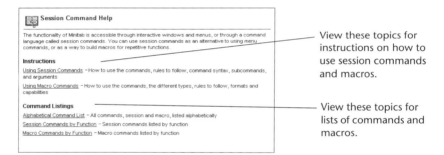

View these topics for instructions on how to use session commands and macros.

View these topics for lists of commands and macros.

 To learn more about session commands, go to Chapter 6, *Using Session Commands*.

**Command-
specific
information**

To access information for a specific session command, at the MTB > command prompt, type *HELP* followed by the command name. Press ⌞Enter⌟.

Most session command topics contain links to:

- **Example** of using the command, including output.
- **See also** links to related topics.

Location of the corresponding command in the Minitab menu.

Command syntax. Click a subcommand to access more detailed information.

Explanation of the command.

Detailed information about subcommands.

What Next

In the next chapter, learn more about the Minitab environment and the types and forms of data that Minitab uses. The chapter also includes a list of quick-reference tables of actions and analyses available in Minitab.

11

Reference

Objectives

In this chapter, you find information about:

- Minitab environment, page 11-2
- Minitab data, page 11-5
- Quick reference, page 11-6

Overview

Previous *Meet Minitab* chapters introduced you to Minitab and some of its features and commands. This chapter provides in-depth information about the Minitab environment and data, as well as quick-reference tables to help you to perform the actions and statistics you need in your own analysis.

The Minitab Environment

As you perform your data analysis, you will work with many different Minitab windows and tools. Here is a brief overview of the Minitab environment:

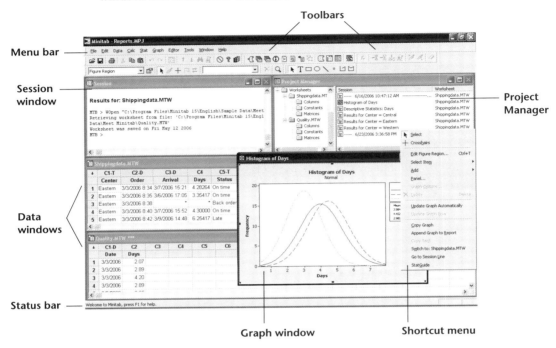

Minitab windows

- The **Session window** displays text output such as tables of statistics. You can display columns, constants, and matrices in this window by choosing **Data ➤ Display Data**.

- **Data windows** contain columns and rows of cells in which you enter, edit, and view the data for each worksheet.

- **Graph windows** display graphs. You can have up to 200 Graph windows open at a time.

Project Manager

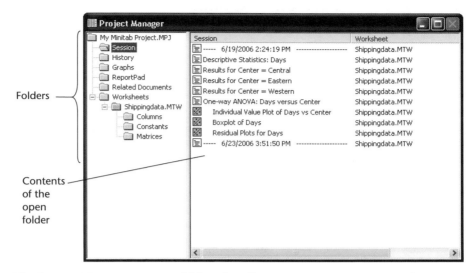

Folders

Contents of the open folder

The Project Manager contains folders that allow you to navigate, view, and manipulate various parts of your project. By right-clicking either the folders or the folder contents, you can access a variety of menus that allow you to manage Session window output, graphs, worksheets, command language, and related project areas.

This folder...	Contains...	Use to...
Session	A list of: ■ All Session window output by command ■ All graphs	Manage Session window output. For example: ■ Jump to Session window output ■ Copy, delete, rename, or print Session window output or graphs ■ Append Session window output or graphs to the ReportPad
History	All commands you have used	■ Repeat complex command sequences ■ Use commands to create Execs and macros
Graph	A list of all graphs in your project	Manage your graphs. For example: ■ Arrange, rename, tile, or remove your graphs ■ Append graphs to the ReportPad

This folder...	Contains...	Use to...
ReportPad	A basic word processing tool	■ Create, arrange, or edit reports of project work ■ Move ReportPad contents to a more powerful word processing program for further editing and layout
Related Documents	A list of program files, documents, or Internet URLs that are related to your Minitab project	Quickly access project-related, non-Minitab files for easy reference
Worksheets	The **Columns**, **Constants**, and **Matrices**, and **Design** folders for each open worksheet	View summaries of worksheet information, including: ■ Column counts, missing values, and column descriptions ■ Constants ■ Matrices ■ Design summary

Menus and tools

Minitab provides:

■ A **menu bar** for choosing commands.

■ A **Standard toolbar** with buttons for commonly used functions–the buttons change depending on which Minitab window is active.

■ A **Project Manager toolbar** with shortcuts to Project Manager folders.

■ A **Worksheet toolbar** with buttons to insert or clear cells, rows, and columns, to move columns, and to move to the next or previous brushed row.

■ A **status bar** which displays explanatory text when you are pointing to a menu item or toolbar button.

■ **Shortcut menus** which appear when you right-click in any Minitab window or any folder in the Project Manager. The menu displays the most commonly-used functions for that window or folder.

■ Graph editing toolbars (**Graph Editing, Graph Annotation Tools,** and **3D Graph Tools**) with buttons for adding and changing graph elements.

■ DOE toolbars (**Factorial Designs, Response Surface Designs, Mixture Designs, Taguchi Designs,** and **OptiPlot**) with buttons for DOE functions.

 Graph editing and DOE toolbars are not visible at start-up, but can be opened by choosing **Tools ➤ Toolbars** and clicking the toolbars you want to show.

Minitab Data

In Minitab, data are contained in a *worksheet*. The number of worksheets a project can have is limited only by your computer's memory.

Data types   A worksheet can contain three types of data:

- *Numeric* data —Numbers.

- *Text* data —Letters, numbers, spaces, and special characters. For example, *Test #4* or *North America*.

- *Date/time* data —Dates (such as Jan-1-2007, 1-Jan-2007, 3/17/07, or 17/03/07), times (such as 08:25:22 AM), or both (such as 3/17/07 08:25:22 AM or 17/03/07 08:25:22 AM). Minitab internally stores dates and times as numbers, but displays them in the format you choose.

Forms of data   Data can be in one of three forms:

Form	Contains...	Referred to by...	Number available
Column	Numeric, text, or date/time data	■ C + number, as in C1 or C22 ■ Column name, such as *Center* or *Arrival*	Limited only by computer memory, up to a maximum of 4000
Stored Constant	A single number or text string (for example, *New York*)	■ K + number, as in K1 or K93 ■ Column name, such as *First* or *Counter*	1000
Matrix	A rectangular block of cells containing numbers	■ M + number, as in M1 or M44 ■ Column name, such as *Inverse*	100

The Project Manager Worksheets folder contains a list of the columns, constants, and matrices in each project.

Sample data sets   Minitab comes with a number of sample data sets. The data sets used in *Meet Minitab* are located in the Meet Minitab folder. You can easily access the sample data sets by clicking **Look in Minitab Sample Data folder** near the bottom of the Open Worksheet dialog box. For complete descriptions of most of these data sets, go to *Sample data sets* in the Minitab Help index.

Quick Reference

To learn where to find commands in Minitab's menus, use the quick-reference tables below. Choose a table and scan the first column for the information you need. The second column in each table tells you where to go in Minitab to perform that action. To find out more about a command, search for the command name in the Minitab Help index.

The quick-reference tables are:

- Projects, page 11-6
- Worksheets, page 11-7
- Toolbars and menus, page 11-8
- Columns, rows, and cells, page 11-9
- Data manipulation, page 11-10
- Data import and export, page 11-12
- Statistics, page 11-12
- Graphs, page 11-20
- Graph windows, page 11-21

Projects

To...	Choose...
Append Session window output to ReportPad	Window ➤ Project Manager ➤ Session folder, then ReportPad folder
Close current project	File ➤ New ➤ Minitab Project File ➤ Open Project File ➤ Exit

To...	Choose...
Copy, delete, rename, or print Session window output or graphs	Window ➤ Project Manager ➤ Session folder
Create macros using commands	Window ➤ Project Manager ➤ History folder
Create new project	File ➤ New ➤ Minitab Project
Edit and execute commands used previously	Edit ➤ Command Line Editor
Edit last dialog box	Edit ➤ Edit Last Dialog
Enter or view project description (creator, date, and comments)	File ➤ Project Description
Exit Minitab	File ➤ Exit
Generate, arrange, and edit reports in ReportPad	Window ➤ Project Manager ➤ ReportPad folder
Jump to specific Session window output	Window ➤ Project Manager ➤ Session folder
Manage graphs (save, copy, print, tile, rename, or append to ReportPad)	Window ➤ Project Manager ➤ Graphs folder
Open existing project	File ➤ Open Project
Open project-related, non-Minitab files, documents, and Internet URLs	Window ➤ Project Manager ➤ Related Documents folder
Password protect project file	File ➤ Save Project As ➤ Security
Repeat complex command sequences	Window ➤ Project Manager ➤ History folder
Run Exec file (type of Minitab macro)	File ➤ Other Files ➤ Run an Exec
Save project	File ➤ Save Project File ➤ Save Project As
View automatically updated summary of current worksheet	Window ➤ Project Manager ➤ Worksheet folder(s)

Worksheets

To...	Choose...
Change data-entry direction (horizontal or vertical)	Editor ➤ Worksheet ➤ Change Entry Direction
Close worksheet	File ➤ Close Worksheet

To...	Choose...
Copy worksheet to new worksheet or append to existing worksheet	Data ➤ Copy ➤ Worksheet to Worksheet
Edit worksheet links (manage links, get external data, and execute external commands)	Edit ➤ Worksheet Links
Enter or view worksheet description (creator, dates, and comments)	Editor ➤ Worksheet ➤ Description
Merge worksheets	Data ➤ Merge Worksheets
Open existing worksheet	File ➤ Open Worksheet
Open new worksheet	File ➤ New ➤ Minitab Worksheet
Print worksheet	File ➤ Print Worksheet
Save current worksheet with new name	File ➤ Save Current Worksheet As
Save current worksheet	File ➤ Save Current Worksheet
Split worksheet	Data ➤ Split Worksheet
Subset all or part of worksheet and copy to a new worksheet	Data ➤ Subset Worksheet

Toolbars and menus

To...	Choose...
Assign keyboard shortcut to command	Tools ➤ Customize, then click Keyboard tab
Create or delete toolbar	Tools ➤ Customize, then click Toolbars tab
Customize menu, submenu, menu bar, or toolbar	Tools ➤ Customize, then click Commands, Toolbars, or Menu tab
Display or hide toolbar	Tools ➤ Customize, then click Toolbars tab
Display toolbar buttons with large icons	Tools ➤ Customize, then click Options tab
Hide or show status bar	Tools ➤ Status Bar
Hide or show toolbar	Tools ➤ Toolbars
Manage user-specific settings	Tools ➤ Manage Profiles
Password protect project file	Tools ➤ File Security

To...	Choose...
Reset Minitab menus	Tools ➤ Customize, then click Menu tab
Set options in Minitab to change defaults to your preferences	Tools ➤ Options
Show or hide screen tips or shortcut keys	Tools ➤ Customize, then click Options tab

Columns, rows, and cells

To...	Choose...
Assign formula to a column, calculate formulas, remove formulas	Editor ➤ Formulas ➤ Assign Formulas to Columns Remove Formulas From Selected Columns Calculate All Formulas Now Calculate All Formulas Automatically
Clear contents of selected cells; leave empty cells or missing-value symbols in their place	Edit ➤ Clear Cells
Combine two or more text columns side by side in new column	Data ➤ Concatenate
Copy columns, constants, and matrices	Data ➤ Copy
Copy contents of selected cells to clipboard	Edit ➤ Copy Cells
Cut cells from worksheet and copy to clipboard	Edit ➤ Cut Cells
Delete cells from worksheet, moving up other rows in column	Edit ➤ Delete Cells
Delete rows from the worksheet	Data ➤ Delete Rows
Enter or view column description	Editor ➤ Column ➤ Description
Erase columns, constants, and matrices	Data ➤ Erase Variables
Format columns (data type, width, standard width for all columns in worksheet, hide or unhide, and define value order)	Editor ➤ Format Column Editor ➤ Column
Go to designated cell	Editor ➤ Go To...

To...	Choose...
Go to next column, active cell, or next/previous brushed row	Editor ➤ Go To ➤ *choose item*
Insert empty cell above selected cell	Editor ➤ Insert Cell
Insert empty column to left of selected column	Editor ➤ Insert Column
Insert empty row above selected row	Editor ➤ Insert Row
Move selected columns to left of designated column, or after last column in use	Editor ➤ Move Columns
Paste contents of clipboard into selected cells	Edit ➤ Paste Cells
Select all cells in worksheet	Edit ➤ Select All Cells
Sort columns and store them in original columns, other columns you specify, or new worksheet	Data ➤ Sort
Stack rows into columns	Data ➤ Stack ➤ Rows
Stack single columns or blocks of columns	Data ➤ Stack ➤ Columns Data ➤ Stack ➤ Blocks of Columns
Transpose columns into rows and store in new worksheet or at end of current worksheet	Data ➤ Transpose Columns
Undo/redo actions	Edit ➤ Undo Edit ➤ Redo
Unstack columns	Data ➤ Unstack Columns

Data manipulation

To...	Choose...
Calculate column statistics, such as mean, median, or standard deviation	Calc ➤ Column Statistics
Calculate probability densities (pdf), cumulative probabilities (cdf), and inverse cumulative probabilities (invcdf) for chosen distribution	Calc ➤ Probability Distributions

To...	Choose...
Calculate row statistics, such as mean, median, or standard deviation, for each row of chosen variables	Calc ➤ Row Statistics
Change data type to/from numeric, text, or date/time	Data ➤ Change Data Type
Change value or set of values to new values (numeric, text, or date/time data to the same or a different type of data, or use conversion table)	Data ➤ Code
Create mesh data for 3D plots	Calc ➤ Make Mesh Data
Define custom lists for Autofill	Editor ➤ Define Custom Lists
Define missing value strings for pasted data	Editor ➤ Clipboard Settings
Display columns, constants, or matrices in Session window	Data ➤ Display Data
Extract one or more parts of date/time data—for example, quarter and year—and put in another column	Data ➤ Extract from Date/Time ➤ To Numeric Data ➤ Extract from Date/Time ➤ To Text
Find/replace data	Editor ➤ Find Editor ➤ Replace
Generate column of ranks for variable	Data ➤ Rank
Generate random data for many distributions, including normal, chi-square, binomial, and Weibull	Calc ➤ Random Data
Make indicator (dummy) variables	Calc ➤ Make Indicator Variables
Make patterned data (simple or arbitrary set of numbers, text values, and simple or arbitrary set of date/time values)	Calc ➤ Make Patterned Data
Set starting point for random data generator	Calc ➤ Set Base
Standardize (center and scale) columns of data	Calc ➤ Standardize

To...	Choose...
Use Calculator to do arithmetic operations, comparison operations, logical operations, functions, column and row operations, and assign formulas to columns	Calc ➤ Calculator
Work with matrices	Calc ➤ Matrices

Data import and export

To...	Choose...
Copy, cut, or paste text in Session window	Edit ➤ Copy Edit ➤ Cut Edit ➤ Paste
Enable or disable command language	Editor ➤ Enable Commands
Find/replace output contents	Editor ➤ Find Editor ➤ Replace
Make output editable or uneditable	Editor ➤ Output Editable
Print Session window	File ➤ Print Session Window
Save Session window output as TXT, RTF, HTM, HTML, or LIS file	File ➤ Save Session Window As
Scroll through output by command	Editor ➤ Next Editor ➤ Previous
Select entire contents of Session window	Edit ➤ Select All
Set fonts to be used in Session window	Editor ➤ Apply Font
View Session window	Window ➤ Session

Statistics

To perform this analysis...	Choose...
Basic statistics	
Calculate column statistics, such as mean, median, or standard deviation	Calc ➤ Column Statistics

To perform this analysis...	Choose...
Calculate row statistics, such as mean, median, or standard deviation, for each row of chosen variables	Calc ➤ Row Statistics
Descriptive statistics	Stat ➤ Basic Statistics ➤ Display Descriptive Statistics Store Descriptive Statistics Graphical Summary
Z- or t-tests	Stat ➤ Basic Statistics ➤ 1-Sample Z 1-Sample t 2-Sample t Paired t
1 or 2 proportions	Stat ➤ Basic Statistics ➤ 1 Proportion 2 Proportions
1- or 2-sample Poisson rate	Stat ➤ Basic Statistics ➤ 1-Sample Poisson Rate 2-Sample Poisson Rate
1 or 2 variances	Stat ➤ Basic Statistics ➤ 1 Variance 2 Variances
Correlation or covariance	Stat ➤ Basic Statistics ➤ Correlation Covariance
Normality test	Stat ➤ Basic Statistics ➤ Normality Test
Goodness-of-fit for Poisson	Stat ➤ Basic Statistics ➤ Goodness-of-Fit Test for Poisson

Regression

Regression (simple/multiple, stepwise, best subsets, or fitted line plot)	Stat ➤ Regression ➤ Regression Stepwise Best Subsets Fitted Line Plot
Partial least squares	Stat ➤ Regression ➤ Partial Least Squares

To perform this analysis...	Choose...
Logistic regression	Stat ➤ Regression ➤ Binary Logistic Regression Ordinal Logistic Regression Nominal Logistic Regression

ANOVA (analysis of variance)

Analysis of variance	Stat ➤ ANOVA ➤ One-Way One-Way (Unstacked) Two-Way Balanced ANOVA General Linear Model Fully Nested ANOVA
Multivariate ANOVA	Stat ➤ ANOVA ➤ Balanced MANOVA General MANOVA
Graphical analysis	Stat ➤ ANOVA ➤ Analysis of Means Interval Plot Main Effects Plot Interactions Plot
Test for equal variances	Stat ➤ ANOVA ➤ Test for Equal Variances

DOE (design of experiments)

Factorial designs (create, analyze, or plot)	Stat ➤ DOE ➤ Factorial ➤ Create Factorial Design Define Custom Factorial Design Select Optimal Design Pre-Process Responses for Analyze Variability Analyze Factorial Design Analyze Variability Factorial Plots Contour/Surface Plots Overlaid Contour Plot Response Optimizer

To perform this analysis...	Choose...
Response surface designs (create, analyze, or plot)	Stat ➤ DOE ➤ Response Surface ➤
	Create Response Surface Design
	Define Custom Response Surface Design
	Select Optimal Design
	Analyze Response Surface Design
	Contour/Surface Plots
	Overlaid Contour Plot
	Response Optimizer
Mixture designs (create, analyze, or plot)	Stat ➤ DOE ➤ Mixture ➤
	Create Mixture Design
	Define Custom Mixture Design
	Select Optimal Design
	Simplex Design Plot
	Factorial Plots
	Analyze Mixture Design
	Response Trace Plot
	Contour/Surface Plots
	Overlaid Contour Plot
	Response Optimizer
Taguchi designs (create, analyze, or plot)	Stat ➤ DOE ➤ Taguchi ➤
	Create Taguchi Design
	Define Custom Taguchi Design
	Analyze Taguchi Design
	Predict Taguchi Results

Control charts

Box-Cox transformation	Stat ➤ Control Charts ➤ Box-Cox Transformation
Variables charts for data in subgroups	Stat ➤ Control Charts ➤ Variables Charts for Subgroups ➤
	Xbar-R
	Xbar-S
	I-MR-R/S (Between/Within)
	Xbar
	R
	S
	Zone

To perform this analysis...	Choose...

Variables charts for individual data points	Stat ➤ Control Charts ➤ Variables Charts for Individuals ➤
	
	    I-MR
	    Z-MR
	    Individuals
	    Moving Range

Attributes charts	Stat ➤ Control Charts ➤ Attributes Charts ➤
	
	    P
	    NP
	    C
	    U

Time-weighted charts	Stat ➤ Control Charts ➤ Time-Weighted Charts ➤
	
	    Moving Average
	    EWMA
	    CUSUM

Multivariate control charts	Stat ➤ Control Charts ➤ Multivariate Charts ➤
	
	    Tsquared-Generalized Variance
	    Tsquared
	    Generalized Variance
	    Multivariate EWMA

Quality tools

Charts	Stat ➤ Quality Tools ➤
	
	    Run Chart
	    Pareto Chart
	    Cause-and-Effect
	    Multi-Vari Chart
	    Symmetry Plot

Process capability	Stat ➤ Quality Tools ➤
	
	    Individual Distribution Identification
	    Johnson Transformation
	    Capability Analysis
	    Capability Sixpack

To perform this analysis...	Choose...
Measurement system analysis	Stat ➤ Quality Tools ➤ Gage Study ➤
	Type I Gage Study Create Gage R&R Worksheet Gage Run Chart Gage Linearity and Bias Study Gage R&R (Crossed) Gage R&R (Nested) Attribute Gage Study (Analytic Method)
Attribute agreement analysis	Stat ➤ Quality Tools ➤ Attribute Agreement Analysis
Acceptance sampling	Stat ➤ Quality Tools ➤
	Acceptance Sampling by Attributes Acceptance Sampling by Variables

Reliability/survival

Test plans	Stat ➤ Reliability/Survival ➤
	Demonstration Test Plans Estimation Test Plans Accelerated Life Test Plans
Distribution analysis –right or arbitrary censoring	Stat ➤ Reliability/Survival ➤ Distribution Analysis ➤
	Distribution ID Plot Distribution Overview Plot Parametric Distribution Analysis Nonparametric Distribution Analysis
Warranty analysis	Stat ➤ Reliability/Survival ➤ Warranty Analysis➤
	Pre-Process Warranty Data Warranty Prediction
Growth curves	Stat ➤ Reliability/Survival ➤ Repairable Systems Analysis ➤
	Parametric Growth Curve Nonparametric Growth Curve
Regression with life data	Stat ➤ Reliability/Survival ➤ Regression with Life Data
Accelerated life testing	Stat ➤ Reliability/Survival ➤ Accelerated Life Testing
Probit analysis	Stat ➤ Reliability/Survival ➤ Probit Analysis

To perform this analysis...	Choose...

Multivariate

Principal components and factor analysis	Stat ➤ Multivariate ➤ Principal Components Factor Analysis
Cluster analysis	Stat ➤ Multivariate ➤ Cluster Observations Cluster Variables Cluster K-Means
Discriminant analysis	Stat ➤ Multivariate ➤ Discriminant Analysis
Correspondence analysis	Stat ➤ Multivariate ➤ Simple Correspondence Analysis Multiple Correspondence Analysis

Time series

Time series plot	Stat ➤ Time Series ➤ Time Series Plot
Ad hoc model fitting techniques	Stat ➤ Time Series Trend Analysis Decomposition Moving Average Single Exp Smoothing Double Exp Smoothing Winters' Method
Differences and lag	Stat ➤ Time Series ➤ Differences Lag
Correlation analysis	Stat ➤ Time Series ➤ Autocorrelation Partial Autocorrelation Cross Correlation
ARIMA	Stat ➤ Time Series ➤ ARIMA

Tables

Tally variables	Stat ➤ Tables ➤ Tally Individual Variables
Cross-tabulation and chi-square	Stat ➤ Tables ➤ Cross-Tabulation and Chi-Square
Chi-square test	Stat ➤ Tables ➤ Chi-Square Test (Two-Way Table in Worksheet)

To perform this analysis...	Choose...
Descriptive statistics	Stat ➤ Tables ➤ Descriptive Statistics

Nonparametrics

Median tests	Stat ➤ Nonparametrics ➤ 1-Sample Sign 1-Sample Wilcoxon Mann-Whitney
Analysis of variance by ranks	Stat ➤ Nonparametrics ➤ Kruskal-Wallis Mood's Median Test Friedman
Test of randomness (runs test)	Stat ➤ Nonparametrics ➤ Runs Test
Pairwise statistics	Stat ➤ Nonparametrics ➤ Pairwise Averages Pairwise Differences Pairwise Slopes

Exploratory data analysis (EDA)

Plots	Stat ➤ EDA ➤ Stem-and-Leaf Boxplot
Analysis	Stat ➤ EDA ➤ Letter Values Median Polish Resistant Line Resistant Smooth Rootogram

Power and sample size

Z- or t-tests	Stat ➤ Power and Sample Size ➤ 1-Sample Z 1-Sample t 2-Sample t
1 or 2 proportion	Stat ➤ Power and Sample Size ➤ 1 Proportion 2 Proportions
One-way ANOVA	Stat ➤ Power and Sample Size ➤ One-Way ANOVA

To perform this analysis...	Choose...

Factorial design	Stat ➤ Power and Sample Size ➤
	
	    2-Level Factorial Design
	    Plackett Burman Design

Graphs

To...	Choose...

Examine relationships between pairs of variables	Graph ➤
	
	    Scatterplot
	    Matrix Plot
	    Marginal Plot

Examine and compare distributions	Graph ➤
	
	    Histogram
	    Dotplot
	    Stem-and-Leaf
	    Probability Plot
	    Empirical CDF
	    Boxplot
	    Probability Distribution Plot

Compare summaries or individual values of variables	Graph ➤
	
	    Boxplot
	    Interval Plot
	    Individual Value Plot
	    Line Plot
	    Bar Chart
	    Pie Chart

Assess distributions of counts	Graph ➤
	
	    Bar Chart
	    Pie Chart

Plot a series of data over time	Graph ➤
	
	    Time Series Plot
	    Area Graph
	    Scatterplot

Examine relationships among three variables	Graph ➤
	
	    Contour Plot
	    3D Scatterplot
	    3D Surface Plot

Display character graphs (must be added via Tools ➤ Customize ➤ Menu)	Character Graphs ➤ *choose graph*

Graph windows

To...	Choose...
Add gridlines, reference lines, data labels, titles, or other items to graph	Editor ➤ Add
Add variables to brushing table	Editor ➤ Set ID Variables
Bring selected annotation element to front or send to back	Editor ➤ Annotation ➤ Bring to Front Editor ➤ Annotation ➤ Send to Back
Brush graphs	Editor ➤ Brush
Change 3D Surface Plot lighting (only available via 3D Graph Tools toolbar)	Tools ➤ Toolbars ➤ 3D Graph Tools
Copy command language of graph, including for editing	Editor ➤ Copy Command Language
Copy graph to paste into another application	Edit ➤ Copy Graph
Copy selected graph text	Editor ➤ Copy Text
Create column that identifies brushed rows	Editor ➤ Create Indicator Variables
Deselect graph element	Editor ➤ Select
Duplicate annotation	Editor ➤ Annotation ➤ Duplicate Annotation
Duplicate graph	Editor ➤ Duplicate Graph
Edit selected element of graph	Editor ➤ Edit *selected element*
Layout different graphs on same page	Editor ➤ Layout Tool
Make similar graph by changing only variables	Editor ➤ Make Similar Graph
Open graph	File ➤ Open Graph
Panel graphs of different groups in same graph window	Editor ➤ Panel
Print graph	File ➤ Print Graph
Rotate 3D graph (only available via 3D Graph Tools toolbar)	Tools ➤ Toolbars ➤ 3D Graph Tools
Rotate selected annotation element	Editor ➤ Annotation ➤ Rotate Left *or* Rotate Right

To...	Choose...
Save graph (Minitab MGF, JPG, TIF, PNG, or Windows BMP)	File ➤ Save Graph As
Select graph element for editing	Editor ➤ Select Item ➤
Show or hide graph annotation toolbar	Editor ➤ Annotation ➤ Graph Annotation Tools
Update graph when data change	Editor ➤ Update
View exact xy coordinates of point on graphs with standard two-variable regions	Editor ➤ Crosshairs
View exact xyz coordinates of point on factorial, response surface, or mixture contour plots	Editor ➤ Plant Flag
Zoom in and out on graph	Editor ➤ Zoom

Index

Numerics

3D Graph Tools toolbar 11-4

A

adding data to a worksheet 4-5
analysis of variance 3-4
    Tukey's multiple comparison
        test 3-4
analyzing data 3-1
annotating graph layout 2-13
annotation, automatic 9-2
ANOVA
    see analysis of variance
Append to Report 7-2
arithmetic functions
    see Calculator
arrow, data entry 4-5
assessing quality 4-1
assign formulas to a column 8-9
Autofill 4-5
automatic footnote, creating 9-2
automating an analysis 6-7

B

boxplots of data 3-5
built-in graphs 2-1, 3-1
    generating 3-5

C

calculate formulas 8-9
Calculator 8-9
capability analysis 4-8
center line 4-2
    interpreting 4-8
changing defaults 9-2
coding data 8-8
columns 1-5, 11-5
    assigning formulas 8-9
    inserting 8-8
    naming 8-8
    number 1-5
    stacking 8-6
Command Line Editor 6-5
command prompt 6-2
confidence intervals 3-6
constants 11-5
contacting Minitab 10-3
control charts 4-2
    adding reference line 4-7
    setting options 4-3
    subgroups 4-3
    updating 4-6
control limit 4-2
Copy to Word Processor 7-7
Cpm value, interpreting 4-10
custom toolbars, creating 9-3
customer support 10-3
customizing Minitab 9-1

D

data
    adding to a worksheet 4-5
    analyzing 3-1
    coding 8-8
    date/time 11-5
    forms 11-5
    merging 8-3, 8-4
    numeric 11-5
    replacing 8-8
    stacking 8-6
    text 11-5
    types 1-5, 11-5
data entry arrow 4-5
data folder, setting default 1-5
data sets, sample 11-6
Data window 1-3
date/time data 11-5
default settings
    changing 9-2
    data folder 1-5
    graphs 2-6
    restoring 9-2, 9-6
descriptive statistics, displaying 3-2
design of experiments (DOE) 5-1
Display Descriptive Statistics 3-2
DOE 5-1

E

editing graphs 2-5
editing in ReportPad 7-5
editing tools for graphs 7-7
effects plots 5-8
Embedded Graph Editor 7-7
environment, in Minitab 11-2
Excel, merging data into worksheet
    8-3
Exec file 6-6
experimental designs 5-1

F

factorial designs 5-1
    analyzing 5-6
    creating 5-2
    effects plots 5-8
    entering data 5-5
    fitting a model 5-6
    interaction plot 5-9
    main effects plot 5-9
    naming factors 5-3
    randomizing run order 5-4
    selecting 5-2
Factorial Designs toolbar 11-4
factorial plots 5-9
files
    HTML format 7-6
    merging 8-3, 8-4
    MPJ file type 2-14
    MTB file type 6-7
    MTW file type 8-2
    opening a worksheet 8-2
    RTF format 7-6, 7-7
    saving projects 2-13
    text 8-4
    types used by Minitab 8-2
    XLS format 8-3
folder
    Graph 11-3
    History 6-5, 11-3
    Related Documents 11-4
    ReportPad 7-2, 11-4
    Session 11-3
    setting default 1-5
    Worksheet 11-4
font, changing in ReportPad 7-5
footnote
    adding to graphs 2-10
    creating automatic 9-2
forms of data 11-5
formula in a column 8-9
four-in-one residual plot 3-8

G

Graph Annotation Tools toolbar 11-4
Graph Editing toolbar 11-4
Graph folder 11-3
Graph windows 11-2
graphing data 2-1
graphs 2-1
    adding reference line 4-7
    adding to ReportPad 7-2
    built-in 2-1, 3-1, 3-5
    changing default settings 2-6
    editing 2-5, 2-10, 7-8
    editing in another application 7-7
    embedded editing tools 7-7
    gallery 2-2
    generating session commands after editing 6-6
    layout tool 2-11
    printing 2-13
    updating 4-5
    viewing 3-11
grouped histogram 2-4
    interpreting 2-5

H

Help 10-1
    accessing 2-8, 10-4
    command-specific information 10-7
    finding information 10-6
    overview 10-4
    session commands 10-10
    StatGuide 10-8
    What's New 10-3
histogram
    grouped 2-4
    grouped, interpreting 2-5
    paneled 2-6
History folder 6-5, 11-3
HTML file format 7-6
hypothesis testing 3-4

I

individual value plot 2-2, 3-5
    interpreting 2-4
information, resources 10-2
inserting a column 8-8
interaction plot 5-9
Internet, Minitab on the 10-3

K

keyboard shortcuts
    assigning 9-5
    default 9-6

L

layout tool for graphs 2-11
    adding annotation 2-13
    printing 2-13

M

macros 6-6
main effects plot 5-9
Manage Profiles 9-6
mathematical functions
    see Calculator
matrices 11-5
menu bar 11-4
merging files 8-3, 8-4
missing values 8-6
mixture designs 5-1
Mixture Designs toolbar 11-4
Move to Word Processor 7-6
MPJ file format 2-14
MTB macro file 6-7
MTW file format 8-2
multiple comparison of means 3-4
    interpreting 3-6
    StatGuide 3-8

N

naming columns 8-8
normal distribution 2-2
normal probability plot of effects 5-8
numeric data 11-5

O

one-way ANOVA 3-4, 3-8
opening a worksheet 1-4, 8-2
options
    setting for Minitab 9-2
    setting for tests for special causes 4-3
OptiPlot toolbar 11-4

P

p-value 3-6
paneled histogram 2-6
Pareto chart of effects 5-8
plots
    effects 5-8
    factorial 5-9
    individual value 2-2, 3-5
    residual 3-5, 3-7
    scatterplot 2-9
preparing a worksheet 8-1
previewing a worksheet 8-4
printing 2-13
process capability 4-8
profiles, managing 9-6
project files, saving 2-13
Project Manager 3-10
    Graph folder 11-3
    History folder 6-5, 11-3
    Info window 8-5
    Related Documents 11-4
    ReportPad 7-2, 11-4
    Session folder 11-3
    Show Graphs icon 3-11

Show Session Folder icon 3-10
    toolbar 3-10, 11-4
    Worksheet folder 11-4

Q

quality 4-1
quick reference 11-6

R

randomizing run order 5-4
ReadMe file 10-3
reference line 4-7
Related Documents folder 11-4
repeating an analysis 6-5
replacing values in a worksheet 8-8
replicates 5-3
ReportPad 7-2, 11-4
    adding graphs 7-2
    adding Session window output 7-3
    changing font 7-5
    editing 7-5
    saving contents 7-6
reports
    copying to word processor 7-6
    saving 7-6
residual plots 3-5
    four-in-one 3-8
    histogram of the residuals 3-7
    normal probability plot 3-7
    residuals versus order 3-7
    residuals versus the fitted values 3-7
response surface designs 5-1
Response Surface Designs toolbar 11-4
restoring default settings 9-2, 9-6
rows 1-5
RTF file format 7-6, 7-7

S

sample data sets 11-6
saving
    Execs 6-6
    project 2-13
    report 7-6
    worksheet 8-11
scatterplot 2-9
    editing 2-10
    interpreting 2-10
Session Command Help 10-10
    command-specific information 10-11
    finding information 10-10
session commands 6-1
    enabling 6-2
    generating for edited graph 6-6
    using 6-1
Session folder 11-3
Session window 1-3, 11-2
    adding output to ReportPad 7-3
    command prompt 6-2
    viewing output 3-3
setting options 9-2
shortcut keys
    assigning 9-5
    default 9-6
shortcut menus 11-4
Show Graphs icon 3-11
Show Session Folder icon 3-10
special causes 4-2
specification limits 4-9
stability 4-2
stacking data 8-6
Standard Toolbar 11-4
starting Minitab 1-3
StatGuide 10-8
    accessing 3-8, 10-8
    command-specific information 10-9
    finding information 10-8
status bar 11-2, 11-4
stored constants 11-5

subgroups 4-3
subscripts 8-7

T

Taguchi designs 5-1
Taguchi Designs toolbar 11-4
target value 4-7, 4-9
    interpreting 4-10
technical support 10-3
tests for special causes 4-2
    setting options 4-3
text
    data 11-5
    files 8-4
time data
    see date/time data
toolbars 11-2
    3D Graph Tools 11-4
    creating custom 9-3
    DOE 11-4
    Factorial Designs 11-4
    Graph Annotation Tools 11-4
    Graph Editing 11-4
    Mixture Designs 11-4
    OptiPlot 11-4
    Project Manager 3-10, 11-4
    Response Surface Designs
      11-4
    Standard 11-4
    Taguchi Designs 11-4
    Worksheet 11-4
Tukey's multiple comparison test
  3-4
    interpreting 3-6
    StatGuide 3-8
typographical conventions 1-2

U

updating a formula 8-10
updating graphs 4-5

V

variables 1-5
    entering in a dialog box 2-3
viewing
    graphs 3-11
    Session window output 3-3

W

Web site 10-3
What's New file 10-3
window
    Data 1-3, 11-2
    Graph 11-2
    Project Manager 11-3
    Session 1-3, 11-2
word processor, copy report to a 7-6
worksheet 1-3
    adding data 4-5
    Autofill 4-5
    entering data 4-5
    merging data from Excel 8-3
    merging data from text file 8-4
    opening 1-4, 8-2
    preparing 8-1
    previewing 8-4
    saving 8-11
    viewing a summary 8-5
Worksheet folder 11-4
Worksheet toolbar 11-4
WWW address 10-3

X

Xbar-S chart 4-3
    interpreting 4-5
XLS file format 8-3

Documentation

To help you use Minitab most effectively, Minitab offers a variety of helpful documentation.

Meet Minitab: *Meet Minitab* is a concise guide to getting started with Minitab software. You can order *Meet Minitab* by contacting your nearest Minitab office, or download the electronic version for free from our website. Simply go to www.minitab.com/products/minitab/15, click the Documentation link, and follow the onscreen instructions.

Minitab Help: This comprehensive, convenient source of information is available at the touch of a key or a click of the mouse. In addition to complete menu and dialog box documentation, you can find overviews, examples, guidance for setting up your data, information on calculations and methods, and a glossary.

Minitab StatGuide™: The online StatGuide explains how to interpret statistical tables and graphs in a practical, easy-to-understand way. The tone is informal and friendly, and it is easily accessible by right-clicking output or by clicking the icon in the toolbar. From basic statistics, to quality tools, to design of experiments, you'll get easy-to-understand guidance when you need it.

Minitab Statistical Glossary: This comprehensive glossary covers all areas of Minitab statistics. Each definition contains practical, easy-to-understand information, including examples and output. You can find it on the Help menu.

Tutorials: The tutorials help you learn Minitab quickly. You can find them on the Help menu.

Companion Text List: The Companion Text List (CTL) is an online bibliographical listing of currently available texts that feature Minitab Statistical Software, including textbooks, textbook supplements, and other related teaching materials. The CTL, updated continuously, is easy to search and a valuable resource for statisticians, teachers, and Minitab users. Check the CTL at www.minitab.com/resources/ctl/.

Minitab Handbook, Fifth Edition: A supplementary text that teaches basic statistics using Minitab, the Handbook features the creative use of plots, application of standard statistical methods to real data, in-depth exploration of data, and more. To order, please contact your nearest Minitab office.

We appreciate your feedback! If you find errors or problems within any of Minitab's documentation, please notify us by e-mailing doc_comments@minitab.com.

Additional Minitab Products

Minitab offers a collection of software, support materials and services that enable you to manage your quality and process improvement processes. Please contact your nearest Minitab office to receive additional information about the following:

Quality Companion by Minitab™: This process management software enables you to organize and Implement the "soft" tasks of process improvement–such as process mapping, brainstorming, and consensus building. Please visit the Minitab website to learn more, take a tour, or try the free trial software.

Quality Trainer by Minitab™: This statistics instructional software helps quality professionals, especially those involved with Six Sigma, learn how to use both statistics and Minitab through a convenient and engaging web-based multi-media course.

Other language products: In our continuing effort to support the global community, Minitab has product and documentation offerings in several languages. Presently, French, German, Japanese, Korean, Portuguese, Spanish, Simplified Chinese, and Traditional Chinese products are available.

Student product: Minitab Student Software is a streamlined and economical version of Professional Minitab, designed specifically for introductory and business statistics courses. It comes bundled with a wide variety of textbooks from leading textbook publishers. This product is for academic use only by degree granting, accredited institutions.

Educational Resources: Explore a wealth of additional educational resources at www.minitab.com/education.

Training by Minitab: A variety of training services are available to help you build the Minitab skills and confidence you need to improve quality. Public and On-Site Training courses are available worldwide, and our Mentoring services offer customers in North America the personalized statistical support they need on a per-project basis. Visit Training by Minitab for details: www.minitab.com/training.

How to Order Additional Products

To order, contact Minitab Inc., Minitab Ltd., Minitab SARL, or your local partner. Contact information is provided on the back cover of this book. Or, visit our web site at www.minitab.com.